Book G

LANGUAGE

gagelearning

© **2002 Gage Learning Corporation**
164 Commander Blvd., Toronto, ON M1S 3C7

Adapted from material developed, designed, and copyrighted by Steck-Vaughn.

We acknowledge the financial support of the Government of Canada
through the Book Publishing Industry Development Program for our
publishing activities.

Editorial Team: Sheree Haughian, Cathy Zerbst
Cover Adaptation: Christine Dandurand

ISBN **0-7715-1038-1**

7 8 9 10 MP 06 05 04 03
Printed and bound in Canada

Table of Contents

Study Skills

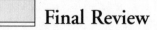 Final Review

> ■ A **synonym** is a word that has the same or nearly the same meaning as one or more other words.
>
>   EXAMPLE: happy—content   cold—chilly

A. Write a synonym for each word below.

1. find _____

2. hard _____

3. sad _____

4. unexpected _____

5. make-believe _____

6. legend _____

7. nervous _____

8. lifelike _____

9. leap _____

B. Rewrite the following sentences, using synonyms for the underlined words.

1. Her broken leg slowly began to <u>heal</u>.

    _____

2. The white cat <u>ran</u> across the room.

    _____

3. The vacationers returned from their trip tired, but <u>happy</u>.

    _____

4. The <u>excited</u> child was <u>beating</u> a drum.

    _____

5. The couple danced <u>gracefully</u> across the floor.

    _____

6. This flower is so <u>beautiful</u>. What is it <u>called</u>?

    _____

7. "Well actually," Sek-Lung <u>said</u>, "I live up the <u>street</u>."

    _____

8. After a long evening babysitting, Anton was <u>exhausted</u>.

    _____

9. The clerk was <u>angry</u> about the computer failure.

Lesson 2
Homophones

> ■ **Homophones** are words that have the same sound but different spellings and meanings.
>
> EXAMPLE: It requires great **patience** to play chess.
> The surgeon has many **patients.**

A. Complete the sentence by writing the correct homophone in the blank.

principal/principle   brake/break   stationary/stationery

lone/loan   days/daze

1. Sheila put her foot on the _____ pedal, but got no response.

2. In order to pay off his car, he had to go to the bank for a _____ .

3. Because he was so seriously injured, it will take _____ before he recovers.

4. I prefer the _____ bike at the gym to riding my 18-speed on icy roads.

5. "The customer is always right" is a basic _____ of business.

6. Dad cried when he saw Liang _____ the Ming vase that had been

   in the family for generations.

7. Yashoo is the _____ partner in the law firm.

8. Mom works from a home office and is always running out of _____ .

9. After the accident, he felt in a _____ .

10. The police report indicated he was the _____ occupant of the vehicle.

B. Write five sentences using homophones. Then remove the homophones and exchange your sentences with a partner and have him or her supply the correct homophone.

1. _____

   _____

2. _____

   _____

3. _____

   _____

4. _____

   _____

5. _____

     Unit 1, Vocabulary

Lesson 3
Homographs

■ A **homograph** is a word that has the same spelling as another word but a different meaning and sometimes a different pronunciation.
EXAMPLE: <u>lead</u>, meaning "go in front," and <u>lead</u>, meaning "a metal"

A. Circle the letter for the definition that best defines each underlined homograph.

1. Ahmed placed the <u>checkers</u> on the board.

   a. small round pieces   **b.** supermarket cashiers   **c.** a pattern of squares

2. <u>Duck</u>, or the tree branches might injure you.

   a. a water bird   **b.** lower the head   **c.** a strong cotton or linen cloth

3. Place the garbage in the <u>can</u>.

   a. to be able to   **b.** to preserve food   **c.** a metal container

4. The baseball player knocked a <u>fly</u> into centre field.

   a. a two-winged insect   **b.** a ball hit with a bat   **c.** to move through the air

B. Write the homograph for each pair of meanings below.

1. **a.** a glass container   **b.** to knock or shake   _____

2. **a.** to observe closely   **b.** a timepiece   _____

3. **a.** a yellow vegetable   **b.** to crush   _____

4. **a.** a fringe of hair   **b.** a loud noise   _____

5. **a.** not heavy   **b.** set fire to   _____

C. Write two sentences for each homograph shown in brackets. Be sure that your sentences reflect the two different meanings of the word.

1. (bat) _____

   _____

2. (saw) _____

   _____

3. (stable) _____

   _____

4. (bark) _____

   _____

5. (fast) _____

   _____

Lesson 4

Prefixes

- A **prefix** added to the beginning of a **root**, or **base word** changes the meaning of the word.
  EXAMPLE: un-, meaning "not" + the root done = undone, meaning "not done"

- Some prefixes have one meaning, and others have more than one meaning.

EXAMPLES:	prefix	meaning
	im-, in-, non-, un-	not
	dis-, in-, non-	opposite of, lack of, not
	mis-	bad, badly, wrong, wrongly
	pre-	before
	re-	again
	sub-	below, in lower position
	micro-	small

A. Add the prefix <u>un-</u>, <u>im-</u>, <u>non-</u>, <u>mis-</u> to the root word in parentheses. Write the new word in the sentence. Use a dictionary if necessary.

1. It is _____ (practical) to put out a monthly newsletter.

2. Robots have been on the moon and, _____ (like) humans, have been to Mars.

3. They will feel quite _____ (comfortable) in such hot weather.

4. Even if the new monkey is _____ (violent) in nature, the others may harm it.

5. Listen carefully, or you might _____ (understand) the question.

B. The following words contain prefixes. Write the meaning of each word.

1. subatomic _____

2. microscope _____

3. disagree _____

4. preview _____

5. misspell _____

6. redo _____

7. subway _____

8. disgrace _____

9. misplace _____

10. impossible _____

- A **suffix** added to the end of a **root**, or **base word** changes the meaning of the word.
    EXAMPLE: -ful, meaning "full of" + the base word <u>joy</u> = <u>joyful</u>, meaning "full of joy"

- Some suffixes have one meaning, and others have more than one meaning.

    EXAMPLES:

suffix	meaning
-able	able to be, suitable or inclined to
-al	relating to, like
-ful	as much as will fill, full of
-er	someone who, more so
-less	without, that does not
-ly	having qualities of, manner or degree
-ous	full of
-tion	forming an action
-y	having, full of

Add a suffix from the list above to the base word in parentheses. Do not use any suffix more than once. Write the new word in the sentence. Check the meaning in your dictionary.

1. Eastern British Columbia is a _____ region. (mountain)

2. If you visit there, it is extremely _____ to have a walking stick to hike the mountain trails. (help)

3. Many skiers visit the province's _____ mountains to ski each year. (snow)

4. On Canada Day, people across the country show a great deal of _____ pride. (nation)

5. The instructor was very_____ about different fishing techniques. (knowledge)

6. _____ , his medical tests were fine. (fortunate)

7. At Tobermory, the _____ went down to explore one of Canada's fine marine parks. (dive)

8. They built a concrete wall along the cliff to offer_____ from the elements. (protect)

9. When drivers become _____ , accidents can happen. (care)

Lesson 6 — Contractions

- A **contraction** is a word formed by joining two other words.
- An **apostrophe** shows where a letter or letters have been left out.
  EXAMPLE: do not = don't
- <u>Won't</u> is an exception. EXAMPLE: will not = won't

A. Underline each contraction. Write the words that make up each contraction on the line.

1. Stingrays look as if they're part bird, part fish. _____

2. Stingrays cover themselves with sand so they won't be seen. _____

3. There's a chance that waders might step on a stingray and get stung. _____

4. That's a painful way to learn that you shouldn't forget about stingrays.

    _____   _____

5. Until recently, stingrays weren't seen very often. _____

6. It doesn't seem likely, but some stingrays will eat out of divers' hands. _____

7. Because its mouth is underneath, the stingray can't see what it's eating.

    _____   _____

8. Once they've been fed by hand, they'll flutter around for more food.

    _____   _____

9. It's hard to believe these stingrays aren't afraid of humans.

    _____   _____

10. To pet a stingray, they'd gently touch its velvety skin. _____

B. Find the pairs of words that can be made into contractions. Underline each pair. Then write the contraction each word pair can make on the lines following the sentences.

1. I have never tried scuba diving, but I would like to.

    _____   _____

2. It is a good way to explore what is under the water.

    _____   _____

3. First, I will need to take lessons in the pool. _____

4. Then I can find out what to do if the equipment does not work. _____

Compound Words

- A **compound word** is a word that is made up of two or more words. The meaning of many compound words is related to the meaning of each individual word.

  EXAMPLE: sand + paper = sandpaper, meaning "a type of paper with a rough surface, used for cleaning or smoothing"

- Compound words may be written as one word, as hyphenated words, or as two separate words. Always check a dictionary.

A. Combine the words in the list to make compound words. You may use words more than once.

work	out	stream
in	base	down
ball	ground	bird
look	air	way
free	sea	cross
walk	lines	under
field	touch	care

1. _____
2. _____
3. _____
4. _____
5. _____
6. _____
7. _____
8. _____
9. _____
10. _____

B. Answer the following questions.

1. Score means to "win points." What is a scoreboard?

   _____

2. Cake is "a baked, sweet food." What is a cupcake?

   _____

3. A neck connects the head and shoulders. What is a necklace?

   _____

4. A fast is "a period of time when a person eats little or nothing." What is breakfast?

   _____

5. Cyber has to do with computers. What is cyberspace?

   _____

Connotation and Denotation

> - The **denotation** of a word is its exact meaning as stated in a dictionary.
>   EXAMPLE: The denotation of <u>casual</u> is "not fancy or formal."
> - The **connotation** of a word is an added meaning that suggests something positive or negative.
>   EXAMPLES: **Positive**: <u>Casual</u> suggests "informal or relaxed."
>   <u>Casual</u> has a positive connotation.
>   **Negative**: <u>Snickered</u> suggests "mocking."
>   <u>Snickered</u> has a negative connotation.
> - Some words are neutral and do not suggest either good or bad feelings.

A. Write (-) if the word has a negative connotation. Write (+) if the word has a positive connotation. Write (N) if the word is neutral.

1. ____ relaxed	4. ____ pushed	7. ____ shoved	10. ____ wrote
2. ____ grand	5. ____ slouched	8. ____ snobby	11. ____ old
3. ____ loud	6. ____ large	9. ____ gang	12. ____ stubborn

B. Rewrite the paragraph below. Replace the underlined words with words that do not a have negative connotation.

The customer <u>stomped</u> into the store and <u>demanded</u> to see the manager. As the manager approached, he <u>glared</u> at her. "I bought these shoes yesterday," he <u>growled</u>. "I wore them once out in the rain, and look, they're already ruined," he <u>barked</u> in a <u>loud</u> tone. "What can you do about it?" he continued <u>belligerently</u>."

"Well, sir, our policy is to give you a new pair of shoes if you're not satisfied with the ones that you've bought," she replied.

"I don't want a new pair," he <u>interrupted</u>, <u>frowning</u> at her suggestion. "What a <u>silly</u> idea! I <u>demand</u> my money back."

_____

_____

_____

_____

_____

_____

_____

_____

_____

Idioms

■ An **idiom** is an expression that has a meaning different from the usual meanings of the individual words within it.

EXAMPLE: <u>We're in hot water</u> means "We're in trouble," not "We're immersed in warm liquid."

A. **Read each sentence. Then write the letter of the corresponding idiom for the underlined word or words.**

A. all ears	**D.** call it a day	**G.** down in the dumps
B. hit the road	**E.** up in the air	**H.** on top of things
C. over the moon	**F.** see red	**I.** come through

_____ **1.** I've done enough work for now. I'm going to <u>quit working</u>.

_____ **2.** When the project was proposed, Hamil was <u>listening intently</u>.

_____ **3.** Amy won a scholarship; she is <u>delighted</u>.

_____ **4.** The day for the picnic is still <u>undecided</u>.

_____ **5.** People who snub others make me <u>angry</u>.

_____ **6.** If we have trouble making the payment, we know dad will <u>help</u>.

_____ **7.** It's past midnight, time for us to <u>leave</u>.

_____ **8.** When Lawrence learned he had failed, he was <u>sad</u> for several weeks.

_____ **9.** After working hard, I finally feel <u>in control of the situation</u>.

B. **Write the usual meaning of the following idioms.**

1. Monica is tired; she's been <u>burning the candle at both ends</u>._____

2. That TV program always <u>cracks up</u> its viewers. _____

3. After the financial loss, our family was really <u>down and out</u>. _____

4. Many of Caleb's ideas seem to be <u>off the wall</u>. _____

5. I can't attend the movie; I'm <u>up to my neck</u> in paperwork. _____

6. Jan is on time <u>once in a blue moon</u>. _____

7. When I make mistakes, my brother likes to <u>rub it in</u>. _____

8. After the accident, the divers were <u>shaken up</u>. _____

9. Interns at the company are considered to be <u>wet behind the ears</u>. _____

Lesson 10

> - A **noun** refers to a person, place, or thing—such as an object, concept, idea, or event. You can use nouns effectively by making them as specific as possible.
>   EXAMPLE: **Original**: The **bird** flew in the sky.
>   **Revised**: The **eagle** flew in the sky.
> - A **verb** is a word or group of words that expresses an action, or a state of being. When verbs are vigorous and descriptive, they provide the reader with a better picture of what is happening.
>   EXAMPLE: **Original**: The eagle **flew** in the sky.
>   **Revised**: The eagle **soared** in the sky.

A. Underline the nouns in the sentences. Where possible, improve the sentence by replacing existing nouns with more effective nouns.

1. Jerry raced down the track in his car. _____

2. Marcel flew across the ocean in a plane. _____

3. I listen to music when I do my homework. _____

4. Davida played an instrument in the band. _____

5. She renovated the room in the old house. _____

6. The truck and car crashed at the intersection. _____

7. The store sells inexpensive things. _____

8. His coat is made of cloth. _____

9. The dog guarded the building. _____

B. Replace the underlined verbs with more effective ones.

1. "I'm going to be late for the concert!" she said. _____

2. "Put the ball in the basket!" spoke the coach. _____

3. In the Olympics, Donovan Bailey ran over the finish line. _____

4. Jennifer and Liam walked to school through the park. _____

5. He saw a light shining from the abandoned building. _____

6. The tiny hummingbird flew from flower to flower. _____

7. The expensive race car travelled to the finish line first. _____

8. The children worked long hours in grimy factories. _____

9. They ate the pizza quickly. _____

     Unit 1, Vocabulary

Review

A. Write S before each pair of synonyms.

___ 1. quiet, silent   ___ 5. risky, precarious   ___ 9. speedy, rapid

___ 2. fearless, bold   ___ 6. calm, serene   ___ 10. cry, wail

___ 3. penniless, destitute   ___ 7. bizarre, normal   ___ 11. astonish, bewilder

___ 4. gentle, harsh   ___ 8. night, darkness   ___ 12. dull, bright

B. Using the homophones in parentheses, write the correct words on the lines.

1. (new, knew) Maria _____ that she would be moving to a _____ city.

2. (through, threw) The player _____ the ball _____ the window.

3. (there, their, they're) _____ sure that _____ friends will be _____ .

4. (it's, its) _____ too early to tell if the dog will lose _____ injured paw.

5. (two, to, too) _____ helpings was _____ much for the child _____ finish.

C. Circle the letter of the best definition for each underlined homograph.

1. The <u>beam</u> in the old barn was rotten.

   a. ray of light   b. large piece of timber   c. smile radiantly

2. The station will <u>air</u> the program at nine this evening.

   a. mixture of gases   b. musical composition   c. broadcast

3. The gift is a <u>mark</u> of her respect.

   a. sign or token   b. impression made by an object   c. unit of German money

4. The officers tried to <u>bar</u> the crowd from the building.

   a. prevent progress   b. counter serving drinks   c. piece of something solid

D. Choose an appropriate prefix or suffix from the box for each of the underlined words below. Write the new word on the line.

| dis- | mis- | re- | un- | -ish | -ful | -less | -ment |

1. to <u>read</u> again _____   6. not <u>civilized</u> _____

2. full of <u>cheer</u> _____   7. act as a <u>fool</u> _____

3. to <u>represent</u> falsely _____   8. without <u>care</u> _____

4. lack of <u>interest</u> _____   9. state of being <u>amazed</u> _____

5. without <u>thanks</u> _____   10. to put in the wrong <u>place</u> _____

E. Underline the pair of words that can be written as a contraction in each sentence. Then write each contraction on the line.

1. Stavros does not want to go swimming. _____

2. I would rather see a good movie. _____

3. It is getting cold. _____

4. Sulu does not like track and field. _____

5. You must not shout at me. _____

6. Who is going to attend summer school? _____

7. Angelo did not wish to vote. _____

F. Combine two words in each sentence to make a compound word. Write the word on the line.

1. The doctor sat at the side of the patient's bed. _____

2. Green plants need to be kept in the house in winter. _____

3. I knocked on the door, but ended up ringing the bell. _____

4. Some flowers require full sun to bloom. _____

5. The lord of the manor owned all the land. _____

G. Write (-) if the underlined word has a negative connotation. Write (+) if the underlined word has a positive connotation.

____ 1. Yolanda is sometimes <u>stubborn</u>.

____ 2. My sister is very <u>enthusiastic</u>.

____ 3. Do you like to <u>gossip</u>?

____ 4. Ryan can <u>gab</u> for hours.

____ 5. Let's <u>dedicate</u> this song to Rehana.

____ 6. They <u>snatched</u> the candy.

____ 7. Those dogs are real <u>pests</u>.

____ 8. I <u>demand</u> that you pay attention.

____ 9. The <u>hovel</u> was very old.

____10. Fran drives an old <u>jalopy</u>.

H. Underline the idiom in each sentence. Then write what the idiom means.

1. The athlete was not content to rest on her laurels. _____

_____

2. The family found it hard to make ends meet. _____

_____

3. The delinquent promised to turn over a new leaf. _____

_____

     Unit 1, Vocabulary

A. Rewrite the following sentences, using synonyms for the underlined words.

1. The lightning flashed across the <u>black</u> sky as the trees <u>bent</u> in the wind.

   _____

2. <u>Blasts</u> of wind whistled through the <u>openings</u> between the boards on the window.

   _____

3. Then a <u>hush</u> seemed to fall over our part of the <u>world</u>.

   _____

B. Write a sentence using a homophone for each word.

1. new _____

2. grater _____

3. choose _____

4. weight _____

5. waist _____

C. For each homograph below, write two sentences. Be sure to use a different meaning of the homograph in each sentence.

1. light a. _____

   b. _____

2. shed a. _____

   b. _____

3. rest a. _____

   b. _____

D. Add one of the following prefixes or suffixes to each base word to make a new word.
Prefixes: in-, non-, dis-, mis-, pre-, re-
Suffixes: -able, -ful, -less

1. place _____   6. tire _____

2. direct _____   7. remark _____

3. use _____   8. spell _____

4. measure _____   9. pay _____

5. speech _____   10. fund _____

E. Use the following idioms in sentences. Use a dictionary if necessary.

1. throw in the towel_____

_____

2. pulling my leg_____

_____

3. skating on thin ice_____

_____

4. get in touch with_____

_____

5. keep an eye on_____

_____

F. Think of words that have almost the same meaning as the neutral word, but have a more negative or positive connotation. Complete the chart with your words.

NEGATIVE CONNOTATION	NEUTRAL	POSITIVE CONNOTATION
1. _____	wet	_____
2. _____	shout	_____
3. _____	house	_____
4. _____	old	_____
5. _____	talk	_____
6. _____	clothes	_____
7. _____	ask	_____

G. Replace the underlined nouns and verbs with more effective words.

1. The baseball player was wearing a <u>hat</u>._____

2. My sister just bought a new <u>car</u>._____

3. The <u>cat</u> had won many show ribbons._____

4. We bought some <u>things</u> at the market._____

5. "I'm in pain," the patient <u>said</u>._____

6. We <u>walked</u> ten kilometres in pouring rain._____

7. Marla <u>looked</u> out the window at the scenery._____

8. The fire truck <u>went</u> to the fire._____

■ A **simple sentence** has one independent clause. It expresses a complete thought, using a **subject** and a **predicate**.

EXAMPLE: The hungry children bought a pie at the farmers' market.
    └──(subject)──┘ └────────(predicate)────────┘

Simple sentences are often brief, but they can be used effectively in writing.

A. Write <u>S</u> before each complete simple sentence, and <u>NS</u> before each example that is not a simple sentence.

_____ **1.** He went to the hospital.

_____ **2.** He bought three oranges, a basket of strawberries, a bag of peas, and three summer squash at the Kitchener market.

_____ **3.** When residents are on holiday, the library closes early.

_____ **4.** The weekend market is a classic example of farmers selling directly to customers and avoiding any attempts by agents to control the supply and adjust the price.

_____ **5.** Sandy was tired of not fitting in.

_____ **6.** Because it was late, we decided to go home.

B. Create effective simple sentences using the following nouns and verbs. The noun is the basis of the subject of the sentence. The verb is the basis of the predicate.

1. apples   tumble

_____

2. children   holler

_____

3. movies   create

_____

4. squirrels   sleep

_____

5. artists   paint

_____

6. horses   gallop

_____

Sentences can be identified by type.

- A **declarative sentence** makes a statement. It is followed by a period.
  EXAMPLE: Lucy is our first dog.

- An **interrogative sentence** asks a question. It is followed by a question mark.
  EXAMPLE: Do you plan on finishing your work?

- An **imperative sentence** expresses a command or a request. It is followed by a period.
  EXAMPLE: Bring it to me.

- An **exclamatory sentence** expresses strong emotion. It can also express a command or request that is made with great excitement. It is followed by an exclamation mark.
  EXAMPLE: How dare you accuse me of stealing!

Write **D** for declarative, **IN** for interrogative, **IM** for imperative, or **E** for exclamatory before each sentence. Put the correct punctuation at the end of each sentence.

_____ 1. I plan to leave by midnight _____

_____ 2. Let your conscience be your guide _____

_____ 3. How do you plan on getting to the party without a car _____

_____ 4. Arrive with your assignment completed _____

_____ 5. There was nothing he couldn't do, nothing _____

_____ 6. Who do we have to thank for the beautiful flowers _____

_____ 7. We were the first ones there _____

_____ 8. I'll have a second helping, if you don't mind _____

_____ 9. Go away _____

_____ 10. What a nice day it is _____

_____ 11. Let's go _____

_____ 12. The boy lay bleeding in the rain _____

_____ 13. Did you fall down, buddy _____

_____ 14. I could walk all day, and never tire _____

_____ 15. Has Amal seen the movie yet _____

_____ 16. Ouch _____

_____ 17. Please leave the room _____

_____ 18. We took the bus to Prince Albert _____

Lesson 13

Inverted Sentences

- When the subject of a sentence comes before the verb, the sentence is in **natural order**.
    - EXAMPLE: Karleen went to the store.

    When the verb or part of the verb comes before the subject, the sentence is in **inverted order**.
    - EXAMPLES: Here are the keys. Down came the snow.
- Many questions are in inverted order.
    - EXAMPLE: Where is the library?
- Sometimes the subject of a sentence is not expressed, as in a command or request. The understood subject is you.
    - EXAMPLE: Call about the bus schedule.

A. Write I to identify the sentences that are in inverted order and N to identify those in natural order.

_____ **1.** I will never forget my first airplane trip.

_____ **2.** There are bookcases on all sides of the room.

_____ **3.** Here are some insights from my experience in the youth movement.

_____ **4.** I am studying with Miguel and Felicia for a math test.

_____ **5.** Who shut the windows?

_____ **6.** He wrote an e-mail to his cousin.

_____ **7.** Down blew the tree.

_____ **8.** Where is the manager?

B. Rewrite each sentence in inverted order. Underline the subject and circle the verb.

1. The calculators are here. _____

2. The car swerved around the curve. _____

3. The skunk scurried under the porch. _____

4. The power went out. _____

5. I will never forget the great October hurricane. _____

6. We have seldom been so sick. _____

7. The deer raced through the woods. _____

8. The new magazines are there. _____

- Every sentence has two main parts, a **complete subject** and a **complete predicate**.
- The complete subject includes all the words that tell who or what the sentence is about.
  EXAMPLES: **My brother**/likes to go with us. **Six geese**/honked loudly.
- The complete predicate includes all the words that state the action or condition of the subject.
  EXAMPLES: My brother/**likes to go with us**. Six geese/**honked loudly**.

A. Draw a line between the complete subject and the complete predicate in each sentence.

1. Bees fly.

2. Trains whistle.

3. A talented artist drew this cartoon.

4. The wind blew furiously.

5. Wood Buffalo is a large national park.

6. We surely have enjoyed the holiday.

7. These cookies are made with rice.

8. This letter came to the post office box.

9. They rent a cabin in the Rockies every summer.

10. Jamila is reading about the pioneer days in the West.

B. Write a sentence by adding a complete predicate to each complete subject.

1. All of the students _____

2. Elephants _____

3. The top of the mountain _____

4. The TV programs tonight _____

5. Each of the girls _____

6. My mother's truck _____

7. The dam across the river _____

8. Our new sports car _____

9. The books in our bookcase _____

10. The mountains _____

- The **simple subject** of a sentence is the main word in the complete subject. The simple subject is a noun or a word that stands for a noun.
  EXAMPLE: My **sister**/lost her gloves.

- Sometimes the simple subject is also the **complete subject**.
  EXAMPLE: **She**/lost her gloves.

- The **simple predicate** of a sentence is a verb within the complete predicate. The simple predicate may be a one-word verb or a verb of more than one word.
  EXAMPLES: She/**lost** her gloves. She/**is looking** for them.

C. Write a sentence by adding a complete subject to each complete predicate.

1. _____ is the largest city in Mexico.

2. _____ came to our program.

3. _____ is a valuable mineral.

4. _____ grow beside the road.

5. _____ travelled day and night.

6. _____ was a great inventor.

7. _____ wrote the letter of complaint.

8. _____ met us at the airport.

9. _____ made ice cream for the picnic.

10. _____ lives near the shopping centre.

D. Draw a line between the complete subject and complete predicate in each sentence below. Underline the simple subject once and the simple predicate twice.

1. A sudden clap of thunder frightened all of us.

2. The soft snow covered the fields and roads.

3. We drove very slowly over the narrow bridge.

4. The students are making an aquarium.

5. Our class read about the founder of Annapolis Royal.

6. The women were talking in the park.

7. This album has many folk songs.

8. We are furnishing the sandwiches for tonight's picnic.

9. All the trees on that lawn are giant oaks.

10. Many Canadians are working in foreign countries.

> ■ A **compound subject** is made up of two or more simple subjects.
> EXAMPLE: **Hiroshi** and **Gina**/are excellent athletes.

A. Draw a line between the complete subject and the complete predicate in each sentence. Write <u>SS</u> for a simple subject. Write <u>CS</u> for a compound subject.

_____ **1.** Omar left the package on the crowded subway.

_____ **2.** She and I will travel to Canmore, Alberta, after Christmas.

_____ **3.** St. John's and Halifax were two cities visited by the tourists.

_____ **4.** The disease spread rapidly to other people in the country.

_____ **5.** Basketball, soccer, and tennis were our favourite sports.

_____ **6.** Tokyo and Osaka are important Japanese cities.

_____ **7.** The Caribbean Sea and the Pacific Ocean are connected by the Panama Canal.

_____ **8.** The Conservatives, the Liberals, and the New Democrats are competing for this riding.

_____ **9.** The crowd waved to us from the station platform.

_____ **10.** Money and power motivate many people.

_____ **11.** Dad washed the dishes left from the party.

_____ **12.** Daffodils and tulips bloom in the spring.

_____ **13.** Our class is studying the anatomy of a frog.

B. Write eight sentences containing compound subjects.

1. _____

2. _____

3. _____

4. _____

5. _____

6. _____

7. _____

8. _____

Compound Predicates

> ■ A **compound predicate** is made up of two or more simple predicates.
> EXAMPLE: Massoud **smiled** and **nodded**.

A. Draw a line between the complete subject and the complete predicate in each sentence. Write <u>SP</u> for each simple predicate. Write <u>CP</u> for each compound predicate.

_____ **1.** People need oxygen to breathe.

_____ **2.** The dealer buys and sells old furniture.

_____ **3.** A flock of geese hissed and honked in the farmyard.

_____ **4.** Mr. Santorini designs and makes amber jewellery.

_____ **5.** *Star Wars* is one of my favourite movies.

_____ **6.** Madhi and Brian were lost in the wilderness.

_____ **7.** Carola participated in the Special Olympics in Calgary.

_____ **8.** They gathered up tin cans for the recycling centre.

_____ **9.** Geraldine's friends are visiting in Yukon and the Northwest Territories.

_____ **10.** The Ecksteins live in that duplex on Avenue Road.

_____ **11.** The groceries were picked up and delivered last night.

_____ **12.** The performers chatted and joked before the play.

_____ **13.** The student has completed six essays this term.

B. Write eight sentences containing compound predicates.

1. _____

2. _____

3. _____

4. _____

5. _____

6. _____

7. _____

8. _____

> ■ The **direct object** tells who or what receives the action of the verb.
>   The direct object is a noun or pronoun that follows an action verb.
>   DO
>   EXAMPLE: The Middle East exports **oil**.

A. Underline the verb in each sentence. Then write <u>DO</u> above each direct object.

1. Every Canadian should have an understanding of federal politics.

2. Do not spend time at the mall every Saturday.

3. Tam, did you keep those stamps for your collection?

4. Olivia Poole invented the Jolly Jumper in 1959.

5. Write the answer in your notebooks.

6. Who explored the Arctic in the nineteenth century?

7. I am reading Margaret Atwood's *Alias Grace*.

8. Who made this delicious ravioli?

9. Did you find an error in that Internet site?

10. Who wrote the biography of Pierre Trudeau?

11. They bought several souvenirs in Niagara Falls.

12. Salvador read the announcement to the astonished team.

13. Did you ever plant a tree on Earth Day?

14. Epidemics have often attacked the region in the winter.

15. Chris brought sushi to the potluck lunch.

B. Write six sentences containing direct objects. Underline the direct object in each sentence.

1. _____

2. _____

3. _____

4. _____

5. _____

6. _____

Lesson 18

> - The **indirect object** is the noun or pronoun that tells to whom or for whom an action is done. In order to have an indirect object, a sentence must have a direct object.
> - The indirect object is usually placed between the action verb and the direct object.
>
>   IO   DO
>   EXAMPLE: Who gave **you** that interesting **book**?

A. Underline the verb in each sentence. Then write <u>DO</u> above each direct object and <u>IO</u> above each indirect object.

1. The artist showed the collectors a few of her paintings.

2. The driving instructor taught them the rules of the road.

3. Joel brought us some new CDs.

4. This fascinating story will give every listener a thrill.

5. Have you sent your uncle an e-mail?

6. They made us some cookies to take on the train.

7. The scientist gave the national Research Council the good news.

8. Bronwen, did you sell Alexei your snowboard?

9. The doctor gave the child a thorough examination.

10. Mom brought her sister a Turkish carpet from Istanbul.

11. Bring me a fork, please.

12. The coach gave the team a long lecture.

13. Show me the photo of your bike.

14. I have given you a cheque for fifty dollars.

15. The club gave the shelter a large donation.

B. Write four sentences containing indirect objects. Underline the indirect object in each sentence.

1. _____

2. _____

3. _____

4. _____

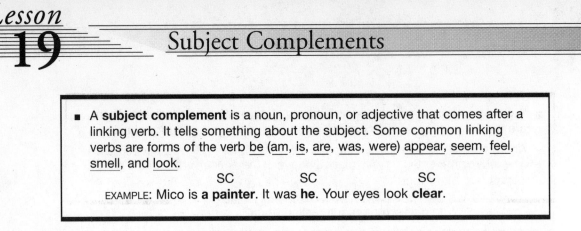

> ■ A **subject complement** is a noun, pronoun, or adjective that comes after a
> linking verb. It tells something about the subject. Some common linking
> verbs are forms of the verb <u>be</u> (<u>am</u>, <u>is</u>, <u>are</u>, <u>was</u>, <u>were</u>) <u>appear</u>, <u>seem</u>, <u>feel</u>,
> <u>smell</u>, and <u>look</u>.
>
>   SC   SC   SC
> EXAMPLE: Mico is **a painter**. It was **he**. Your eyes look **clear**.

A. Underline the verb in each sentence. Then write <u>SC</u> above each subject complement.

1. The grass felt soft under my feet.

2. Rivka was once a police officer.

3. She seemed upset with the results of her exam.

4. The blankets feel soft.

5. Marcia appeared tired after her long hike in the Rockies.

6. Baking bread smells wonderful.

7. The hockey player looked angry when the penalty was called.

8. Who is the person who made the Nanaimo bars?

9. The singer was a candidate for a Juno award.

10. Otto's parents were unclear about their plans for a holiday in Québec.

11. We felt sorry for the victims of the Red River flood.

12. The patient looked better after the treatment.

B. Write sentences using the verbs in brackets. Underline the subject complement.

1. (feel)_____

2. (is)_____

3. (looked)_____

4. (appear)_____

5. (seem)_____

6. (smell)_____

7. (were)_____

                Unit 2, Sentences

> - A clause is a group of words that contains a subject and a predicate. There are two kinds of clauses: **independent clauses** and **subordinate clauses**.
> - An **independent clause** can stand alone as a sentence because it expresses a complete thought.
>   EXAMPLE: **She found the wallet** that she had lost.

A. Underline the independent clause in each sentence below.

1. We arrived early because we took a taxi.

2. The concert started after we had found our seats.

3. We heard the songs that had been featured on the CD.

4. When I was a little girl, my grandmother used to tell us stories about all the stars.

5. After we left the auditorium, we tried to catch a bus to the station.

6. Although the wait was long, we finally managed to find transportation.

7. While we were on the bus, I saw two people from my class at school.

8. Since you left, Uri has been lonely.

9. I saw the actor who had starred in that film.

> - A **subordinate clause** has a subject and predicate, but cannot stand alone as a sentence because it does not express a complete thought.
> - A subordinate clause must be combined with an independent clause to make a sentence.
>   EXAMPLE: We got out of bed **when the alarm clock woke us**.

B. Underline the subordinate clause in each sentence below.

1. Canada is a country where many cultures live together.

2. While we were at the fair, I saw lots of people eating cotton candy.

3. When rules are unfair, everyone suffers the consequences.

4. The rat is an animal that many people fear.

5. Kim is the one who should get credit for the project.

6. If you want to succeed in business, you will have to work hard.

7. We walked along the road until we came to a snack bar.

8. Andrea found a present that was perfect for her best friend's birthday.

9. This bat, which catches harmful insects, should not be feared.

C. Place an <u>I</u> before the clause if it is an independent clause. Place an <u>S</u> before the clause if it is a subordinate clause.

_____ **1.** Jeremy got free tickets to the Expos game

_____ **2.** because he works in the Olympic Stadium ticket office

_____ **3.** the Morgans took the wrong route

_____ **4.** when they came to the cloverleaf on the highway

_____ **5.** who spoke to me

_____ **6.** he is the police officer

_____ **7.** although few of them appear elsewhere

_____ **8.** lake cottages are popular in central Canada

_____ **9.** Mozart was a musical genius

_____**10.** who died young

_____**11.** although Andreas was busy

_____**12.** dogs barked

_____**13.** since neither of them arrived

D. For each subordinate clause, provide an independent clause to create a complete sentence.

1. _____

2. _____

3. _____

4. _____

5. _____

6. _____

7. _____

- An **adjective clause** is a subordinate clause that modifies a noun or a pronoun. It answers the adjective questions Which one? Or What kind? It usually modifies the word directly preceding it. Most adjective clauses begin with a **relative pronoun**. A relative pronoun relates an adjective clause to the noun or pronoun that the clause modifies. Who, whom, whose, which, and that are relative pronouns.
    EXAMPLE: Never take chances with ice **that isn't frozen**.
                                                          adjective clause

- An **adverb clause** is a subordinate clause that modifies a verb, an adjective, or another adverb. It answers the adverb question How? Under what condition? Or Why? Words that introduce adverb clauses are called **subordinating conjunctions**. The many subordinating conjunctions include such words as when, after, before, since, although, and because.
    EXAMPLE: We departed **when the speeches were over**.
                                        adverb clause

A. **Underline the subordinate clause. Then write <u>adjective</u> or <u>adverb</u> on the line.**

_____ **1.** John Franklin was an explorer who lost his life in the Arctic.

_____ **2.** The writer who wrote this book won the Giller Prize.

_____ **3.** He was late because his car broke down.

_____ **4.** Scrub the floor when you are finished the baking.

_____ **5.** The dog growled at the shadow that looked real.

_____ **6.** Nothing has happened since you left.

B. **Add a subordinate clause beginning with the word in parentheses to each independent clause below.**

1. We travelled to Thailand (after) _____

_____

2. A museum is a place (where) _____

_____

3. The man died (before) _____

_____

4. Find me someone (who) _____

_____

When writing, it's a good idea to use a variety of sentence lengths and types. When there are too many short sentences, the writing can seem very jerky. One way to correct this problem is by combining short sentences to create a longer compound sentence.

■ A **compound sentence** consists of two or more independent clauses. The clauses are joined by using conjunctions such as <u>or</u>, <u>and</u>, or <u>but</u>.

EXAMPLE:

Two simple sentences: I don't know where he went. No one has seen him since this morning.

Combined into a compound sentence: I don't know where he went, and no one has seen him since this morning.

Combine the simple sentences below to create compound sentences.

1. James Rederfree was born in the West Indies. James Rederfree spent most of his life in Ottawa.

_____

_____

2. Harriet could not see any pedestrians. Harriet drove through the intersection. _____

_____

3. So Oscar agreed. Oscar set off to visit Emma and Monique. _____

_____

4. Before leaving she walked around the office. Then she turned off the light and closed the door.

_____

_____

5. The trail lay buried under a thick blanket of snow. The tracker could still follow it perfectly.

_____

_____

6. The street rose very steeply. It twisted and turned. _____

_____

7. The day was humid. The hikers managed to reach their destination. _____

_____

8. I really enjoy hiking. I think I like biking even better. _____

_____

- A **complex sentence** consists of one independent clause and one or more subordinate clauses.
    - EXAMPLE: When the announcement was made, he went to the office.
        (subordinate clause)   (independent clause)

- A **compound sentence** consists of two or more independent clauses. Each independent clause in a compound sentence can stand alone as a separate sentence. Independent clauses are usually joined by such words as <u>and</u>, <u>but</u>, <u>so</u>, <u>or</u>, <u>for</u>, or <u>yet</u>.
    - EXAMPLE: My sister is athletic, **and** my brother is musical.

A. Write <u>CX</u> before each complex sentence. Write <u>CP</u> before each compound sentence.

_____ **1.** I may not have the best bike in the world, but it suits me.

_____ **2.** You can loiter outside the mall, but I have to go to work.

_____ **3.** The workers who patrol the park must know every centimetre of the grounds.

_____ **4.** I hadn't seen Laetitia for a long time, and I had never been to Calgary.

_____ **5.** Saul and Mike get together whenever they can.

_____ **6.** The double-play ball was thrown perfectly, but the player on first base missed it.

_____ **7.** That song, which you keep hearing on the radio, was written by a Canadian.

_____ **8.** We made hot dogs for dinner, and then we ate ice cream.

_____ **9.** When it started to snow, everyone headed for the ski hill.

_____**10.** The town was on the map, but all you could see was an overpass.

_____**11.** The thunder struck, and rain began to fall.

_____**12.** The mayor, who was elected in November, said taxes won't rise.

_____**13.** When she arrives, Miranda will take charge.

_____**14.** The apples were cooked perfectly, but the potatoes were burned.

B. For each complex sentence you identified, underline the independent clause and circle the subordinate clause or clauses. For each compound sentence, underline the independent clauses.

Combining Sentences

> ■ Using a variety of sentence types helps to create variety for the reader. You can combine related **simple sentences** to create **complex** or **compound sentences**.
>
> EXAMPLE: My mother's family lives in Pakistan. My father's family lives in Scotland. (two **simple sentences**)
>
> **Complex sentence**: My mother's family lives in Pakistan, while my father's family lives in Scotland.
>
> **Compound sentence**: My mother's family lives in Pakistan, and my father's family lives in Scotland.

Combine the following simple sentences to make compound or complex sentences.

1. I was thirteen years old. I went on a trip with my mother. We went to a town called Coutts.

_____

2. We were in the border office for almost two hours. We talked to almost everyone there.

_____

3. Hurricanes are fascinating to watch on TV. I wouldn't advise experiencing one in person.

_____

4. Forest fires destroy great amounts of timber. The fires can affect the lives of many people.

_____

5. John A. Macdonald was Canada's first prime minister. He promoted expansion of the railroad.

_____

6. The movie was entertaining. It seemed long in places.

_____

7. Abdul is my cousin. He came to visit last September.

_____

8. We had a detailed map. We still got lost.

_____

9. Vancouver is in British Columbia. It is an interesting city.

_____

- Sentences can be **expanded** by adding details to make them clearer and more interesting.   EXAMPLE: The horse galloped. The **wild grey** horse galloped **around the field, nostrils flaring.**
- Details added to sentences may answer these questions: When? Where? How? How often? To what degree? What kind? Which? How many?

A.   Expand each sentence below by adding details to answer the questions shown in parentheses. Write the expanded sentence on the line.

1. The team was ready to play. (Which? When?)

   _____

2. The cat purred. (What kind? Why?)

   _____

3. The wind roared. (Which? How?)

   _____

4. The dog ran. (What kind? Why?)

   _____

5. The scientists studied the ozone layer. (How many? Where? Why?)

   _____

B.   Decide how each of the following sentences can be expanded. Write your expanded sentence on the line.

1. The athlete ran into the arena.

   _____

2. The kids ate.

   _____

3. The bird began to sing.

   _____

4. The musician strummed the guitar.

   _____

5. The fox scurried.

   _____

6. The audience cheered.

Sentence Fragments

> ■ A **sentence fragment** is a phrase or clause that might look like a sentence, but does not express a complete thought. The fragment might be missing an important element of sentences, such as a verb or subject.
> EXAMPLE: **Fragment**: Just before eating.
> **Corrected sentence**: Just before eating, he phoned his girlfriend.

A. **Place an F to indicate which of the following is a sentence fragment or an S to indicate if it is a complete sentence.**

_____ **1.** While serving her residency at a Manitoba hospital.

_____ **2.** Clyde refused.

_____ **3.** To be a member of the Royal Ontario Museum expedition to Costa Rica.

_____ **4.** Who discovered that insulin was a treatment for diabetes.

_____ **5.** As long as the government continues to provide subsidies.

_____ **6.** It requires dedication to become a full-time writer.

_____ **7.** In the heart of cottage country.

_____ **8.** Since the Homestead Act was repealed.

_____ **9.** Stop!

_____**10.** Inevitably, things change.

B. **Identify the sentence fragments in the following paragraph. Then, rewrite the paragraph using complete sentences.**

Fall. My favourite season of the year. In fall I can do a lot of my favourite things. Hike, play touch football, watch the baseball playoffs. During fall in Gander, there are special events. Fall fairs, cross-country runs, barn dances. Just drive in the country. You'll see a panorama of colours. Reds, brown, oranges, brilliant yellows. Reflecting off the water. What a sight.

_____

_____

_____

_____

_____

Lesson 27

Run-On Sentences

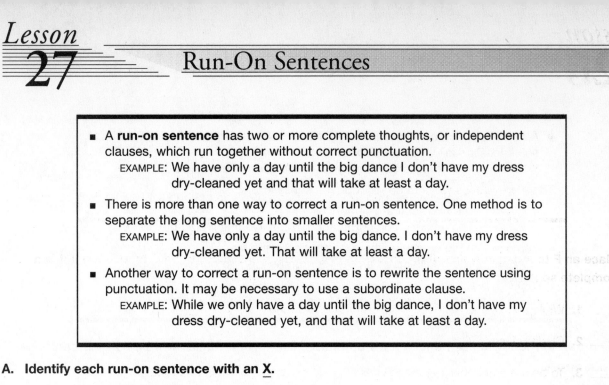

- A **run-on sentence** has two or more complete thoughts, or independent clauses, which run together without correct punctuation.
  EXAMPLE: We have only a day until the big dance I don't have my dress dry-cleaned yet and that will take at least a day.

- There is more than one way to correct a run-on sentence. One method is to separate the long sentence into smaller sentences.
  EXAMPLE: We have only a day until the big dance. I don't have my dress dry-cleaned yet. That will take at least a day.

- Another way to correct a run-on sentence is to rewrite the sentence using punctuation. It may be necessary to use a subordinate clause.
  EXAMPLE: While we only have a day until the big dance, I don't have my dress dry-cleaned yet, and that will take at least a day.

A. Identify each run-on sentence with an X.

_____ 1. With a mighty blow I swung the bat the ball sailed out of the park.

_____ 2. The prime minister spoke at great length on CBC radio.

_____ 3. I bought two sweaters one has to be returned.

_____ 4. The magazine sells for a loonie in Canada it cost 70¢ in the United States.

_____ 5. Our Winnipeg relatives arrived in the middle of a storm.

_____ 6. Seanna won the race she defeated six rivals.

B. Correct the following run-on sentences.

1. Justine plays hockey she plays for a team that tours Canada.

_____

2. The rock star cancelled his performance it was the second time in two weeks.

_____

3. City lots are too expensive for most people the cost is discouraging.

_____

4. Sybil was surprised and enthusiastic her design won a prize at the tech fair.

_____

5. The ice has melted it's spring at last.

_____

6. It's too early to get up let me sleep longer.

_____

- A **comma splice error** occurs when two closely related but independent sentences are joined by a comma.
    EXAMPLE: The house stood empty for months, no one would buy it.

There are various ways to correct comma splice errors.

- You can create two separate sentences.
    EXAMPLE: The house stood empty for months. No one would buy it.

- You can turn the sentence into a compound sentence.
    EXAMPLE: The house stood empty for months, and no one would buy it.

- You can use a semicolon to join the two sentences.
    EXAMPLE: The house stood empty for months; no one would buy it.

A. Some of the following sentences have comma splice errors. Place an X beside the sentences with errors.

_____ **1.** She is going to the dentist, but not to have a cavity fixed.

_____ **2.** The patient was sent home, nothing more could be done.

_____ **3.** The convention ended on Saturday, we can return to work Friday.

_____ **4.** Remarkably, he didn't have a clue.

_____ **5.** We took the bus, it was late afternoon when we arrived in Antigonish.

_____ **6.** My friend was as pale as white chalk, he had frightened eyes.

_____ **7.** We went to the dance, even though we should have been studying.

_____ **8.** Ian is incredibly kind, he helps people in need almost every day.

_____ **9.** The astronaut thanked her colleagues, who had been supportive throughout the mission.

_____ **10.** The higher you climb, the farther you can fall.

B. Correct the comma splice errors you found above. Use each solution at least once.

1. _____

2. _____

3. _____

4. _____

5. _____

_____

_____

A. Label each sentence as follows: Write **D** for declarative, **IN** for interrogative, **IM** for imperative, or **E** for exclamatory. Write **X** if it is not a sentence. Punctuate each sentence correctly.

_____ **1.** Did they arrive on time _____

_____ **2.** Be brave _____

_____ **3.** Curled up on the couch_____

_____ **4.** Everyone went to the game _____

_____ **5.** Help, I'm stuck_____

_____ **6.** Where is your hat _____

_____ **7.** Oh, watch out _____

_____ **8.** Teens from all over Canada_____

_____ **9.** Lin swam four kilometres_____

_____**10.** Put the book down _____

B. Rewrite each sentence in natural order.

1. At the bottom of the hill lay a child thrown from a toboggan.

_____

2. Under the sea, live many new species.

_____

C. In each sentence below, underline the words that are identified in parentheses.

1. (complete subject) The man in the dark overcoat left.

2. (simple subject) Parks are in all parts of our country.

3. (direct object) Trista collects coins for a hobby.

4. (complete predicate) We ambled slowly down the street.

5. (simple predicate) We noticed a strange light.

6. (compound predicate) Sasha sings and dances quite well.

7. (compound subject) Pizza and hamburgers are sold at that variety store.

8. (indirect object) The company gave our team new sweaters.

9. (subject complement) Good dogs are obedient at all times.

10. (indirect object) Please lend me some money, so I can buy ice cream.

D. Write **S** after each simple sentence, **CP** after each compound sentence, and **CX** after each complex sentence.

_____ **1.** We bought a modem and a scanner at the sale.

_____ **2.** Beatrice, who is very popular, invited her friends to a barbecue.

_____ **3.** The candidate that I voted for won the election easily.

_____ **4.** We will go now and they will join us later.

_____ **5.** Renata will take out her canoe after it has been repaired.

E. Underline the independent clause, and circle the subordinate clause in each sentence. Write adjective clause or adverb clause on the line after each sentence.

1. Entomologists are scientists who are trained to study insects._____

2. Before I left for Regina, I paid all my bills._____

3. The meal that Semil prepared included soup and salad._____

4. Although the horse was old, it was not vicious._____

5. Many people surf the Net because they want to find information._____

F. Combine the following sentences to form a compound or a complex sentence.

1. Biking is Signe's favourite sport. Baseball is Kurt's favourite sport.

_____

2. The water was icy cold. We didn't go swimming until the sun was hot.

_____

3. Soon it will be September. They will return to school.

_____

4. The food was delicious. We asked for seconds.

_____

5. Snow fell last night. It caused several highways to close.

_____

G. Underline the sentence fragments in the following paragraph.

    Thanksgiving at my aunt's. The family gathers on the weekend, and we enjoy some of my favourite food. Turkey, mashed potatoes, cranberry sauce, and incredible pumpkin pie. Somehow a meal is more enjoyable. When you take a walk afterwards on a cold clear night. Stars dot the sky. Last year my sister and I saw the Northern Lights.

H. Identify each run-on sentence with an RO. Place a CS before sentences containing a comma splice.

_____ 1. Shara couldn't have predicted the fire, although she may have known of some danger.

_____ 2. The detective looked for evidence she checked all surfaces of the room thoroughly.

_____ 3. The cottage was abandoned by its owners, it was beginning to fall apart.

_____ 4. Laughter is extremely contagious, spread it to others.

_____ 5. Money is no object to that family, they eat in restaurants every night.

_____ 6. Sven was displeased with the news because it made more work for him.

_____ 7. No one knew her secret, even her parents were not aware of her illness.

                                                   Unit 2, Sentences

Using What You've Learned

A. Read the sentences in the box. Then answer the questions below.

> **A.** Did I send you enough food?
>
> **B.** This Internet site is amazing!
>
> **C.** Be at the school by nine o'clock.
>
> **D.** You and I can go shopping tomorrow.
>
> **E.** We can hike and swim after lunch.

_____ 1. Which sentence has a compound subject?

_____ 2. Which sentence has a compound predicate?

_____ 3. Which sentence has a direct object?

_____ 4. Which sentence has an indirect object?

_____ 5. Which sentence is interrogative?

_____ 6. Which sentences are declarative?

_____ 7. Which sentence is exclamatory?

_____ 8. Which sentence is imperative?

_____ 9. Which sentence has a subject complement?

10. What is the complete subject of **E**? _____

11. What is the simple subject of **E**? _____

12. What is the simple predicate of **C**? _____

B. Rewrite each inverted sentence below in natural order.

1. Reported on the radio was the news of the robbery.

   _____

2. Into the driveway zipped the red Ferrari.

   _____

3. Down the street wandered the stray dog.

   _____

4. Out of the station roared the fire engine.

   _____

C. Underline the verb in each sentence. Then write DO above each direct object, IO above the indirect objects, and SC above each subject complement.

1. Mr. Luengo took his elderly neighbour a chicken casserole.

2. The musician showed her agent a new composition.

3. We felt sorry for the homeless people on the street.

4. Helmut, please send your boss a fax.

D. Create compound or complex sentences by adding an independent or a subordinate clause to each group of words.

1. Before we left Bombay, _____

2. She won the Governor General's Award _____

3. I am delighted _____

4. This was the place _____

E. Read the two sentences below. Then expand each sentence by adding details to make the sentence more interesting.

1. The cheetah ran. _____

2. The artist painted a scene. _____

F. Rewrite the sentence fragments into interesting complete sentences.

1. In the depths of the ocean. _____

2. Camping in Alberta. _____

G. Rewrite the paragraph below, correcting the run-on sentences and comma splice errors.

Chocolate is a food made from the seeds of a cacao tree, the tree produces the beans from which all chocolate is made. These trees flourish in a warm, moist climate they live in an area close to the equator. Workers cut the pods from the trees with knives attached to long poles, or with machetes, they gather the pods into heaps, cut them open, and scoop out the beans. The beans are dried and shipped to factories, there, they are processed into a substance called chocolate liquor. Many kinds of chocolate products are then manufactured.

_____

_____

_____

_____

_____

_____

- There are two main classes of nouns: **common** and **proper nouns**.
- A **common noun** names any one of a class of objects.
  EXAMPLES: boy, country, flower
- A **proper noun** names a particular person, place, or thing. It begins with a capital letter.
  EXAMPLES: Ms. Pavlov, Halifax, Parliament Buildings

A. Underline each noun. Then write C or P above it to show whether it is a common or proper noun.

1. Levi is my best friend.

2. Victoria is the chief city on Vancouver Island and capital of British Columbia.

3. The Magdalen Islands are located in the Gulf of St. Lawrence.

4. A killer tornado ripped through southern Ontario last May.

5. John Bassett II and Elmer Iseler, two famous Canadians, died in April 1998.

B. Write a proper noun suggested by each common noun.

1. city _____   8. sea _____

2. magazine _____   9. train _____

3. politician _____   10. bay _____

4. province _____   11. musician _____

5. athlete _____   12. holiday _____

6. university _____   13. newspaper _____

7. rock star _____   14. mountain _____

C. Write a sentence using each proper noun and the common noun for its class.

1. Ethiopia _____

2. Dominik Hasek _____

3. Nunavut _____

4. Canada Day _____

5. Celine Dion _____

6. Atlantic _____

- A **concrete noun** names things you can see and touch.
  EXAMPLES: sea, book, train, hotel
- An **abstract noun** names an idea, quality, or feeling.
  EXAMPLES: cowardice, stubbornness, jealousy
- A **collective noun** names a group of persons or things.
  EXAMPLES: audience, crowd, committee

D. **Classify each common noun as concrete, collective, or abstract. In some cases a noun may fit into two categories.**

1. fleet _____
2. management _____
3. school board _____
4. truthfulness _____
5. flock _____
6. justice _____
7. virtuousness _____
8. umbrella _____
9. litter _____
10. honour _____
11. plywood _____
12. people _____
13. pride _____
14. team _____
15. pencil _____
16. envy _____

E. **Create meaningful sentences using the nouns in brackets. Note that collective nouns usually take a singular verb.**

1. (honesty) _____
2. (jury) _____
3. (motorbikes) _____
4. (family) _____
5. (courage) _____
6. (lake) _____
7. (orchestra) _____
8. (mountains) _____
9. (anger) _____
10. (herd) _____
11. (photo) _____
12. (audience) _____

The following chart shows how to change **singular nouns** into **plural nouns**.

Noun	Plural Form	Examples
Most nouns	Add -s	ship, ships nose, noses
Nouns ending in a consonant and -y	Change the -y to -i, and add -es	sky, skies navy, navies
Nouns ending in -o	Add -es or -s	hero, heroes solo, solos
Most nouns ending in -f or -fe	Change the -f or -fe to -ves	half, halves
Most nouns ending in -ch, -sh, -s, or -x	Add -es	bench, benches bush, bushes
		loss, losses tax, taxes
Many two-word or three-word compound nouns	Add -s to the principle word	son-in-law, sons-in-law
Nouns with the same form in the singular and plural	No change	sheep
Nouns that are exceptions to the rules		woman, women

A. Fill in the blank with the plural form of the word in parentheses.

1. (knife) These are dull _____.

2. (dish) That restaurant on Queen Street serves tasty _____.

3. (country) What _____ are in Central America?

4. (deer) There are many _____ in the park.

5. (piano) These _____ came from Germany.

6. (fly) How many _____ did you kill?

7. (hose) There are two _____ in the garage.

8. (fax) Did you send the _____ to the office?

9. (wrench) The store carries many types of _____.

10. (tomato) Do you like fried _____?

11. (calf) Please help feed the _____.

12. (mother-in-law) Both _____ came to their New Year's brunch.

13. (piece) How many _____ of cake did you eat?

14. (family) Several _____ gathered for a barbecue.

15. (branch) The _____ of the tree were damaged by the storm.

16. (video) The store on the corner sells CDs and _____ .

B. Write the correct plural form for each singular noun. Note that some nouns are exceptions to the rules.

1. piglet _____
2. hobo _____
3. duck _____
4. chef _____
5. lunch _____
6. collector _____
7. tragedy _____
8. echo _____
9. niece _____
10. floor _____
11. hand _____
12. county _____
13. mouse _____
14. carriage _____
15. wish _____

16. church _____
17. elf _____
18. desk _____
19. man _____
20. sheep _____
21. wife _____
22. pony _____
23. banjo _____
24. tree _____
25. sight _____
26. watch _____
27. city _____
28. spoonful _____
29. nation _____
30. dome _____

C. Rewrite the sentences, changing each underlined singular noun to a plural noun.

1. The hero saved the child from the burning building. _____

2. Dan took five photo of the reindeer. _____

3. They travelled to several country during their vacation. _____

4. Put the fish you catch into the wooden box. _____

5. Tell us the story of the wolf who roamed the woods. _____

6. Her son-in-law and brother attended the ceremony. _____

7. The man ate the cherry and the peach. _____

8. The book fell from the shelf. _____

9. The builder made the house from brick. _____

10. What legend did the elder tell? _____

 Unit 3, Grammar and Usage

Lesson 31

Possessive Nouns

- A **possessive noun** shows possession of the noun that follows.
- Form the possessive of most singular nouns by adding an apostrophe (') and -s.
  EXAMPLES: the girl's car   Mr. Lewis's book
- Form the possessive of a plural noun ending in -s by adding only an apostrophe.
  EXAMPLES: the Wongs' home   boys' jeans   brothers' business
- Form the possessive of a plural noun that does not end in -s by adding an apostrophe and -s.
  EXAMPLES: children's clothes   women's shoes

A. Write the possessive form of each noun.

1. girl _____

2. child _____

3. women _____

4. children _____

5. Ramji _____

6. baby _____

7. boys _____

8. teacher _____

9. Dr. Ray _____

10. ladies _____

11. brother _____

12. soldier _____

13. men _____

14. aunt _____

15. Ms. Jones _____

B. Rewrite each phrase using a possessive noun.

1. the cap belonging to Jim _____

2. the wrench that belongs to Kathy _____

3. the smile of the baby _____

4. the car that my friend owns _____

5. the new shoes that belong to Aron _____

6. the collar of the dog _____

7. the golf clubs that Maryla owns _____

8. the shoes that belong to the runners _____

9. the friends of our parents _____

10. the opinion of the editor _____

11. the lunches of the children _____

12. the coat belonging to Saul _____

13. the assignment of the teacher _____

- **Verbs** are words or groups of words that express an action, or a state of being. Verbs that express a state of being are sometimes called linking verbs, because they link the subject to another word that describes the subject.
    EXAMPLES: The police **broke** through the door. (action)
    The professor **seems** depressed this morning. (state of being)

- The **present tense** of a verb tells what is happening now.
    EXAMPLE: I **reside** in Calgary.

- The **past tense** tells about something that happened in the past.
    EXAMPLE: I **resided** in Calgary for the first six months of last year.

- The **present participle** is formed by adding -ing to the present tense of the verb, and then using a form of the helping verb be with the present tense.
    EXAMPLE: I am **residing** in Calgary right now.

- The **past participle** is formed by adding -ed to the present tense of a verb to make it past tense, and then using a form of the helping verb have with the past participle.
    EXAMPLE: I have **resided** in Calgary for two years.

Underline the verb or verbs in each sentence. Indicate whether the verb form is present, present participle, past, or past participle.

_____ 1. She took me with her the day she left.

_____ 2. The runner bounds over every hurdle he encounters.

_____ 3. It has helped to have your advice.

_____ 4. The horror of the documentary upset us immensely.

_____ 5. David has changed since Grade Eight.

_____ 6. Stan is barking up the wrong tree.

_____ 7. Hoa has worked in Toronto for five years.

_____ 8. She recalled the woman in the strange robe.

_____ 9. Elena speaks several languages.

_____ 10. My mother is starting a new career.

_____ 11. Elm trees on that street are dying.

_____ 12. We worked as counsellors at a camp in Muskoka.

_____ 13. Who wants more ice cream?

_____ 14. Victor's grandmother emigrated from Hungary.

_____ 15. They have lost several files in a computer crash.

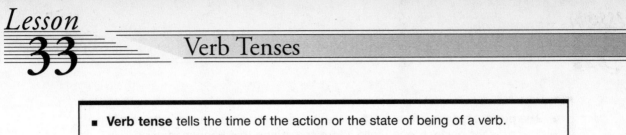

- **Verb tense** tells the time of the action or the state of being of a verb.
- The **present tense** tells what is happening now.
  EXAMPLE: Savitri loves her husband.
- The **past tense** tells about something that happened in the past.
  EXAMPLE: Savitri loved her husband.
- The **future tense** tells about something that will happen in the future.
  EXAMPLE: They will meet again when the war is over.
- A common writing error is inconsistency in verb tenses.

A. Rewrite this paragraph so that it is set in the past.

Jesse picks me up from the airport. She seems to be edgy. She mutters about the traffic most of the drive to the downtown core. This welcome back depresses me, but I quickly get accustomed to the pace of big-city life again.

_____

_____

_____

B. Rewrite this paragraph so that it is set in the present.

Moving as lazily as the flies that droned above the lemon pie, the waitress pushed two cups across the counter. She called to the red-haired young man who was looking intently out the window of the roadside diner. A smile flickered in his flat brown eyes as he handed her a two-dollar coin.

_____

_____

_____

C. Rewrite this paragraph so that it is set in the future.

The applications for this technology are far-reaching. The special system allows companies to track shipments. It also helps keep people safe in countries with high rates of kidnapping.

_____

_____

_____

D. Write a paragraph set in the present, past, or future. Be sure that the verb tenses are consistent.

_____

_____

_____

Lesson 34

Present Perfect and Past Perfect Tenses

- The **perfect tenses** express action that happened before another time or event.
- The **present perfect tense** tells about something that happened at an indefinite time in the past. The present perfect tense consists of has or have + the past participle.
  - EXAMPLES: I **have eaten** already. He **has eaten**, too.
- The **past perfect tense** tells about something that happened before something else in the past. The past perfect tense consists of had + the past participle.
  - EXAMPLE: I already **had eaten** when they arrived.

A. Write present perfect and past perfect for the tense of the underlined verbs.

_____ 1. Lu <u>had completed</u> high school in Vancouver.

_____ 2. We <u>had gone</u> to the restaurant before coming home.

_____ 3. Reuben <u>has decided</u> that he likes skateboarding.

_____ 4. She <u>had been worried</u> that she would fall.

_____ 5. Mei <u>has lived</u> in Saint John for eight years.

_____ 6. We <u>have tried</u> to open the locked door.

_____ 7. Zoe <u>has told</u> us a great deal about tropical plants.

_____ 8. We <u>had known</u> that her injury was serious.

_____ 9. The Inuk storyteller <u>has described</u> things we never knew!

_____ 10. They <u>have decided</u> that they would like to meet their cousins.

B. Complete each sentence with have, has, or had to form the verb tense indicated in parentheses.

1. (present perfect) The dog _____ eaten the ham on the table.

2. (present perfect) The coach and trainer _____ told her to aim high.

3. (past perfect) The doctor _____ warned him to stop smoking.

4. (present perfect) Gaetan _____ taken his place on the podium.

5. (past perfect) Ingrid _____ pitched ten games by the end of last season.

6. (present perfect) The diver _____ located pieces from the shipwreck.

7. (past perfect) The lacrosse team _____ won every game last season.

8. (present perfect) Our neighbours _____ moved to New Brunswick.

9. (past perfect) We _____ heard news of the accident.

10. (past perfect) Indira _____ been elected as committee leader.

  Unit 3, Grammar and Usage

> - Never use a helping verb with: froze, chose, spoke, and broke.
> - Always use a helping verb with: frozen, chosen, spoken, and broken.

A. Underline the correct verb form to complete each sentence.

1. Haven't those politicians (spoke, spoken) yet?

2. Has the ice (froze, frozen) on the pond?

3. Rumina (broke, broken) the handle of the baseball bat.

4. Hadn't the coach (chose, chosen) the best players before?

5. The baby has (broke, broken) the toy.

B. Write the correct past tense form of the verb in parentheses to complete each sentence.

1. (break) The chain on Anya's bicycle had _____ while she raced.

2. (choose) Sumil had _____ to be in the parade.

3. (speak) No one _____ while the orchestra played.

4. (choose) Lim _____ not to go to the gym early.

5. (freeze) The air was so chilly that everything had _____ .

> - Never use a helping verb with came, rang, drank, knew, and threw.
> - Always use a helping verb with come, rung, drunk, known, and thrown.

C. Underline the correct verb.

1. The panting dog (drank, drunk) from the cold lake.

2. The telephone has not (rang, rung) for him today.

3. Martha (knew, known) that he had lied about the gift.

4. Have you (threw, thrown) the newspaper out?

D. Write a sentence using each verb below.

1. come _____

2. rang _____

3. threw _____

4. drunk _____

5. known _____

> ■ Never use a helping verb with gave, took, and wrote.
> ■ Always use a helping verb with given, taken, and written.

E. Underline the correct verb.

1. Who (wrote, written) the best essay?

2. Have you (gave, given) her name to the police?

3. Haven't you (took, taken) your seat yet?

4. Mario had his picture (took, taken) at the mall yesterday.

5. A friend (gave, given) us the furniture for our new apartment.

F. Write the correct past tense form of each verb in parentheses to complete the sentences.

1. (take) Sonya recently _____ a photo of a beluga whale.

2. (write) My friend had _____ to say that he was coming to Moncton.

3. (give) Mr. Ling _____ me a call as soon as he arrived.

4. (take) Before I knew it, the thief had _____ my wallet.

5. (give) The doctor had _____ me a prescription for the infection.

6. (write) "You have _____ a good review of the movie," he said.

> ■ Never use a helping verb with ate, fell, drew, drove, and ran.
> ■ Always use a helping verb with eaten, fallen, drawn, driven, and run.

G. Underline the correct verb.

1. When we had (drove, driven) for three hours, we (began, begun) to feel tired.

2. After Dana had (ate, eaten) breakfast, she (ran, run) around the block.

3. A famous architect (drew, drawn) the plans for the sports centre.

4. Last summer we (drove, driven) to Lake Louise for a holiday.

5. All of the leaves have (fell, fallen) from the maple trees.

H. Write the correct past tense form of each verb in parentheses to complete the sentences.

1. (draw) Since Salma knew the city well, she _____ a map for us.

2. (fall) The police warned us that hydro wires had _____ on the highway.

3. (drive) Ira claimed that he had never _____ under such difficult circumstances.

4. (run) "I almost _____ off the road in the fog!" Rachel exclaimed.

5. (eat) In order to avoid crowds at the snack bar, we _____ our dinner later.

  Unit 3, Grammar and Usage

> - Never use a helping verb with <u>saw</u>, <u>went</u>, and <u>began</u>.
> - Always use a helping verb with <u>seen</u>, <u>gone</u>, and <u>begun</u>.

I. Underline the correct verb.

1. Who has (went, gone) for the pizza?

2. Marla and Yoko (began, begun) to rake the fallen leaves.

3. They had (saw, seen) a meteor.

4. Yes, we (saw, seen) the ad for the free puppies.

5. Our friends have (went, gone) snowmobiling on the open trails.

J. Write a sentence using each verb below.

1. saw _____

2. seen _____

3. gone _____

4. went _____

5. began _____

> - Never use a helping verb with <u>did</u>.
> - Always use a helping verb with <u>done</u>.
> - <u>Doesn't</u> is the contraction of <u>does not</u>. Use it with singular nouns and the pronouns <u>he</u>, <u>she</u>, and <u>it</u>.
>   EXAMPLES: Hannah **doesn't** live here. It **doesn't** work properly.
> - <u>Don't</u> is the contraction of <u>do not</u>. Use it with plural nouns and with the pronouns I, <u>you</u>, <u>we</u>, and <u>they</u>.
>   EXAMPLES: Mr. and Mrs. Truong **don't** have teenagers.
>   You **don't** have your wallet.

K. Underline the correct verb.

1. Please describe what damage the vandals (did, done).

2. (Doesn't, Don't) those pears look overly ripe?

3. The scarf and the sweater (doesn't, don't) match.

4. (Doesn't, Don't) the carpet in our basement smell musty?

5. He has (did, done) me a favour more than once.

L. Write one sentence using <u>did</u> and one sentence using <u>done</u>.

1. _____

_____

2. _____

_____

- Use <u>may</u> to ask for permission.
  - EXAMPLE: **May** I go with you?
- Use <u>can</u> to express the ability to do something.
  - EXAMPLE: Jacques **can** swim well.

A. Complete each sentence with <u>may</u> or <u>can</u>.

1. Mara, _____ you whistle?

2. Her dog _____ do three difficult tricks.

3. Ms. Wong, _____ I leave work early?

4. I _____ see the airplane in the distance.

5. Adam, _____ you tie a good knot?

6. Carla, _____ I drive your car?

7. You _____ see the mountains from here.

8. My friend _____ drive us home.

9. The Kestings _____ speak three languages.

10. _____ I examine those new books?

- Teach means "to give instruction."
  - EXAMPLE: I'll **teach** you how to shoot free throws.
- Learn means "to acquire knowledge."
  - EXAMPLE: When did you **learn** to speak Vietnamese?

B. Complete each sentence with <u>teach</u> or <u>learn</u>.

1. I think he will _____ me quickly.

2. I will _____ to recite that poem.

3. Did Sairah _____ you to build a fire?

4. We are going to _____ to use the new machines.

5. Will you _____ me to play tennis?

6. My sister is going to _____ David to skate.

7. Would you like to _____ the rules of the game to them?

8. No one can _____ you if you do not try to _____ .

Unit 3, Grammar and Usage

Lesson 37

Using *Sit/Set* and *Lay/Lie*

> - <u>Sit</u> means "to take a resting position." Its principal parts are <u>sit</u>, <u>sitting</u>, and <u>sat</u>.
>   EXAMPLES: Please **sit** here. He **sat** beside her.
> - <u>Set</u> means "to place." Its principal parts are <u>set</u>, <u>setting</u>, and <u>set</u>.
>   EXAMPLES: Will you please **set** this dish on the table?
>   He **set** the table for dinner last night.

A. Underline the correct verb.

1. Please (sit, set) down, Karleen.

2. Where should we (sit, set) the TV?

3. Pilar, please (sit, set) those plants out this afternoon.

4. Kim usually (sits, sets) on this side of the table.

5. Please come and (sit, set) your books down on that desk.

> - <u>Lie</u> means "to recline" or "to occupy a certain space." Its principal parts are <u>lie</u>, <u>lying</u>, <u>lay</u>, and <u>lain</u>.
>   EXAMPLES: Why don't you **lie** down for a while?
>   He has **lain** in the hammock all afternoon.
> - <u>Lay</u> means "to place." Its principal parts are <u>lay</u>, <u>laying</u>, and <u>laid</u>.
>   EXAMPLES: The men **are laying** new carpeting in the house.
>   Who **laid** the wet towel on the table?

B. Underline the correct verb.

1. Where did you (lie, lay) your gloves, Felix?

2. (Lie, Lay) down, Rover.

3. He always (lies, lays) down to rest when he is very tired.

4. Where have you (lain, laid) the evening paper?

5. Please (lie, lay) this box on the desk.

C. Complete each sentence. Underline the correct verb in brackets.

1. (Lay, Lie) the papers _____

2. Oscar has (laid, lain) on the couch _____

3. (Sit, Set) the basket _____

4. Amanda (laid, lain) the shovel _____

5. We (sit, set) near _____

- A **singular subject** requires a **singular verb**.
  EXAMPLE: **Kirsten spread** the feast on the table.

- A **plural subject** requires a **plural verb**.
  EXAMPLE: **Her grandmother and her father were** born in Hungary.

- **Collective nouns** usually require a **singular verb**.
  EXAMPLE: My **family speaks** two languages.

- When a phrase containing a plural noun separates a singular subject and a verb, the verb is singular.
  EXAMPLE: An **understanding** of air **currents helps** meteorologists predict weather.

A. Underline the subject and the verb in the following sentences.
Write **Y** if they agree, and **N** if they do not agree.

_____ **1.** The team play soccer every Wednesday evening.

_____ **2.** The picture of those mountains is beautiful.

_____ **3.** A group of teenagers are making a presentation.

_____ **4.** Cats sleep more than any other animal.

_____ **5.** A friend of those people is no friend of mine.

B. Write sentences using the subjects and verbs provided. Be sure that the subject and verb agree.

1. (women) (invent) _____

2. (food) (remain) _____

3. (team) (work) _____

4. (parents) (travel) _____

5. (committee) (organize) _____

6. (insect) (fly) _____

7. (family) (celebrate) _____

8. (orchestra) (play) _____

9. (media) (promote) _____

10. (jury) (convict) _____

Lesson 39

Using *Is/Are* and *Was/Were*

> - Use <u>is</u> with a singular subject.
>   EXAMPLE: Tasha **is** the winner.
> - Use <u>are</u> with a plural subject.
>   EXAMPLE: The boys **are** walking home.
> - Always use <u>are</u> with the pronoun <u>you</u>.
>   EXAMPLE: You **are** absolutely right!

A. Underline the correct verb to complete each sentence.

1. (Is, Are) this tool ready to be cleaned?

2. Martina (is, are) the chairperson this week.

3. Where (is, are) my gloves?

4. This tomato (is, are) too ripe.

5. Iqbal, (is, are) these your books?

> - Use <u>was</u> with a singular subject to tell about the past.
>   EXAMPLE: I **was** there yesterday.
> - Use <u>were</u> with a plural subject to tell about the past.
>   EXAMPLE: Kevin and Ray **were** not home.
> - Always use <u>were</u> with the pronoun <u>you</u>.
>   EXAMPLE: You **were** only a few minutes late.

B. Underline the correct verb to complete each sentence.

1. Amy and Yolanda (was, were) disappointed because they could not go.

2. Everybody (was, were) at my house this morning.

3. Taro, Bill, and Luis (was, were) assigned to the first team.

4. These pencils (was, were) made by a company in Winnipeg.

5. There (was, were) only one package of cookies in the cupboard.

C. Complete each sentence. Underline the correct verb in brackets.

1. Carola asked if you (is, are) _____

2. The shipment of books (was, were) _____

3. Those tomatoes from southern Ontario (was, were) _____

4. Everyone from that town (is, are) _____

5. The committee (was, were) _____

6. She (is, are) _____

7. The Great Lakes (was, were) _____

8. Mechanical engineers (is, are) _____

Unit 3, Grammar and Usage

© 2000 Gage Educational Publishing Company

53

■ **Voice** refers to the relation of a subject to the action expressed by the verb.

■ In the **active voice**, the subject does the action.
EXAMPLE: Robin **made** the dress last year.

■ In the **passive voice**, the subject is acted upon.
EXAMPLE: The dress **was made** last year.

■ Try to avoid overusing the passive voice in writing.

A. Underline each verb. Then write active or passive on the line.

_____ **1.** Under my father's direction, I was taught to be a bricklayer.

_____ **2.** As a child, I happily played with frogs and snakes.

_____ **3.** The songs were written by David Foster.

_____ **4.** Andrew flopped into the chair.

_____ **5.** They passed directly overhead, not half a metre from us.

B. Rewrite each sentence, using the active voice.

1. The telephone was invented by Alexander Graham Bell.

_____

2. With this law, computer crimes will be punished severely.

_____

3. The boat was carried to the landing by the strong wind.

_____

4. March 21 was declared a special day by the United Nations in memory of those who died in Sharpeville, South Africa.

_____

_____

5. A press conference will be given at 6:00 P.M. by Alice Munro.

_____

_____

Pronouns and Antecedents

> - A **pronoun** takes the place of one or more nouns or a group of words in a sentence. Like nouns, pronouns can be used to refer to a person, place, or thing.
>   EXAMPLE: The conductor described the songs we would play. **She** wanted us to memorize **them**. (**She** and **them** are pronouns. They refer to <u>conductor</u> and <u>songs we would play</u>, which are called antecedents.)
>
> - Some common pronouns include <u>I</u>, <u>it</u>, <u>its</u>, <u>me</u>, <u>he</u>, <u>she</u>, <u>we</u>, <u>them</u>, <u>himself</u>, <u>herself</u>, <u>this</u>, <u>that</u>, <u>those</u>, <u>any</u>, <u>some</u>, <u>everyone</u>, <u>who</u>, and <u>what</u>.
>
> - Confusion can occur when it is unclear to which antecedent the pronoun refers.
>   EXAMPLES:
>   **Vague:** The basketball player asked for a meeting in the general manager's office to discuss his new contract. The general manager said she couldn't do **that**. (<u>That</u> is a pronoun. Is the general manager declining the meeting or the discussion?)
>   **Revised:** The basketball player asked if he could meet with the general manager in her office. The general manager said she couldn't do **that**. (The antecedent for <u>that</u> is now clear.)

A. **Underline the pronoun or pronouns in each sentence below. Circle the antecedent. Connect the pronoun and antecedent with a line.**

1. The Member of Parliament was overjoyed because she was re-elected for the second time.

2. Be sure to put sufficient postage on the package before mailing it.

3. The trees that were planted in the sun doubled their growth.

4. Hassan left the magazines exactly as they were when he first saw them.

5. The space shuttle fired its booster rockets.

6. The two waiters spilled food when they bumped into the chef.

7. The crooks left the scene before they could be caught.

8. The woman convinced herself that the news could not be true.

9. The teenagers ate the food, knowing it was not good for them.

10. The doctor was pleased that the patient remembered her.

11. Bianca checked the e-mail and then printed it.

12. Sharif and I aren't sure when we will arrive in Vancouver.

13. The police officer told the children they should be home by dark.

14. The tennis player was surprised when she won the match.

15. The teacher told the boy to get himself organized.

B. The pronoun antecedents are unclear in the following sentences. Underline the pronouns in each, then rewrite the sentences so the antecedent is clear.

1. Dan is teaching, working on his thesis, and writing. He has no idea when he will be finished this.

   _____

2. I really like reading mystery novels, but I like reading non-fiction books too. I enjoy reading them all the time.

   _____

3. He wanted to cut the lawn, wash his car, and drive to Windsor that weekend. This was unrealistic.

   _____

4. After the baseball game, Joshua and Lucio are going to his house to watch TV.

   _____

5. I completed the essay, which pleased my teacher.

   _____

6. Felicia is going to the party with Jenna. They are going in her car.

   _____

7. When Hong visited her aunt in July, she did not know that she was ill.

   _____

8. Henri first met Pierre in Montréal when he was eighteen.

   _____

9. Ask the boys to prepare the vegetables by washing and cutting them with knives.

   _____

10. If the dog leaves any food in his bowl, throw it out.

    _____

11. Pets should not roam loose when visitors come unless they are well-behaved.

    _____

12. If the furnace is repaired, it will save money.

    _____

- A **relative pronoun** is a pronoun that can introduce a subordinate clause. The relative pronouns are who, whom, whose (referring to persons); which (referring to things); and that (referring to persons or things).

- A **subordinate clause**, when introduced by a relative pronoun, serves as an adjective. It modifies a word, or antecedent, in the main clause.
  EXAMPLES: Sylvie knows the writer **whose** novel we read in class.
  The doctor for **whom** I work is from Cambodia.
  The movie **that** won the award is playing downtown.

A. Underline each relative pronoun, and circle its antecedent.

1. It was Mario who played the most difficult role in the play.

2. Stephen Leacock, who wrote many humorous stories, was from Orillia, Ontario.

3. The store that sold movies and video games is going out of business.

4. My aunt lives in a bungalow that was built during the Great Depression.

5. The lamp, which is made of stained glass, was designed a hundred years ago.

6. Did you see the skunk that scurried across the highway?

7. For our holiday dinner, we roasted a ham that weighed three kilograms.

8. This novel, which was written by Rohinton Mistry, is most interesting.

9. We ate the tasty tourtière that Yves had bought at the market.

10. This is the watercolour that was stolen from the gallery.

11. The skates that you want are on sale at a great price.

12. The only food that they have is stale bread and mouldy cheese.

13. A rare bird that winters in the tropics has been sighted in Montréal.

14. A. Y. Jackson is the Canadian artist whose work they most admire.

15. The aquarium is a tourist attraction that is also important to marine research.

16. Yasmeen is the person whose experience was the most positive.

17. We moved to a town that had a large arena.

B. Write sentences containing subordinate clauses that are introduced with the relative pronouns in brackets.

1. (who) _____

2. (which) _____

3. (that) _____

4. (whose) _____

5. (whom) _____

> - Use <u>who</u> as a subject pronoun. EXAMPLE: **Who** came to the party?
> - Use <u>whom</u> as an object pronoun. EXAMPLE: **Whom** did the nurse help?
> - By rearranging the sentence <u>The nurse did help **whom**</u>?, you can see that <u>whom</u> follows the verb and is the object of the verb. It can also be the object of a preposition. EXAMPLE: To **whom** did you wish to speak?

Complete each sentence with <u>Who</u> or <u>Whom</u>.

1. _____ is that man?

2. _____ made the first moon landing?

3. _____ would you choose as the winner?

4. _____ is your best friend?

5. _____ gets the reward?

6. _____ will be staying with you this summer?

7. _____ did the instructor invite to speak to the class?

8. _____ did you see at the park?

9. _____ will you contact at headquarters?

10. _____ will you write about?

11. _____ is available to babysit for me on Saturday?

12. _____ did you drive to the store?

13. _____ would like to travel to Vancouver Island next summer?

14. _____ raced in the track meet?

15. _____ did they meet at the airport?

16. _____ are your three favourite authors?

17. _____ owns that new blue car?

18. _____ did you help last week?

19. _____ wrote that clever poem?

20. _____ will you ask to help you move?

Lesson 44   Adjectives

- An **adjective** is a word that modifies a noun or pronoun. It can describe, limit, or identify the noun or pronoun.
    - EXAMPLE: She likes **oatmeal** cookies.

- A **descriptive adjective** adds details and answers the question, <u>What is it like?</u>
    - EXAMPLES: **fresh** vegetables, **white** cat

- A **limiting adjective** makes the noun or pronoun it modifies more specific and concrete. Some common limiting adjectives are <u>few</u>, <u>many</u>, <u>every</u>, <u>each</u>, <u>both</u>, <u>several</u>, <u>some</u>, <u>any</u>, <u>most</u>, and <u>one</u>. Limiting adjectives such as <u>a</u>, <u>an</u>, and <u>the</u> are also known as **articles**.
    - EXAMPLES: **a** pineapple, **each** apple, **both** parents

- A **proper adjective** is an adjective that is formed from a proper noun. It always begins with a capital letter.
    - EXAMPLES: **Chinese** newspaper, **English** language

A. Underline the adjectives in the following sentences.

1. Grandma kept the valuable pendant in a tiny envelope made of red silk.

2. We managed to get an excellent table at the new Portuguese restaurant.

3. When Dad doesn't have any time to cook, I make some pasta.

B. Write three adjectives to describe each noun.

1. lanterns   _____   _____   _____

2. night   _____   _____   _____

3. shoes   _____   _____   _____

C. The following sentences have few adjectives. Rewrite them using descriptive adjectives.

1. The dog rolled in the mud.

   _____

2. He entered the house during the storm.

   _____

3. The model is wearing a leather jacket.

   _____

4. His sister stuck her hands into water.

   _____

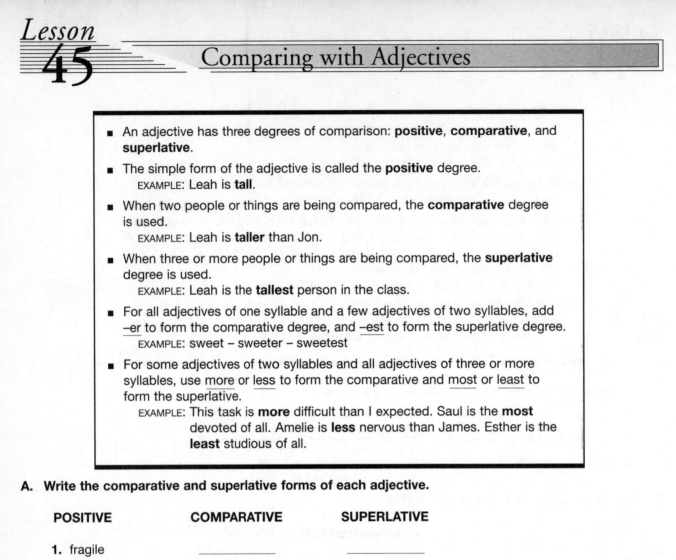

- An adjective has three degrees of comparison: **positive**, **comparative**, and **superlative**.

- The simple form of the adjective is called the **positive** degree.
  EXAMPLE: Leah is **tall**.

- When two people or things are being compared, the **comparative** degree is used.
  EXAMPLE: Leah is **taller** than Jon.

- When three or more people or things are being compared, the **superlative** degree is used.
  EXAMPLE: Leah is the **tallest** person in the class.

- For all adjectives of one syllable and a few adjectives of two syllables, add –er to form the comparative degree, and –est to form the superlative degree.
  EXAMPLE: sweet – sweeter – sweetest

- For some adjectives of two syllables and all adjectives of three or more syllables, use more or less to form the comparative and most or least to form the superlative.
  EXAMPLE: This task is **more** difficult than I expected. Saul is the **most** devoted of all. Amelie is **less** nervous than James. Esther is the **least** studious of all.

A. Write the comparative and superlative forms of each adjective.

POSITIVE	COMPARATIVE	SUPERLATIVE
1. fragile	_____	_____
2. soft	_____	_____
3. silent	_____	_____

B. Complete each sentence with the correct degree of comparison of the adjective given in parentheses. Some of the forms are irregular.

1. (mild) The temperature seems _____ this month than last.

2. (fast) The cheetah is the _____ of all animals.

3. (athletic) Is Farah _____ than Jennifer?

4. (busy) The video store is the _____ store on the block.

5. (deep) Which is the _____ ocean, the Atlantic or the Pacific?

6. (lovely) I think Lake Louise is the _____ of all mountain lakes.

7. (tasty) That restaurant makes the _____ souvlaki in the city.

8. (high) Which of the two balloons flew _____ ?

9. (entertaining) Which is _____ , a stand-up comic or a TV sitcom?

Lesson
46

Adverbs

- An **adverb** is a word that modifies a verb, an adjective, or another adverb.
  - EXAMPLES: "No," Hannah said **stubbornly**.
  - His temper was **extremely** volatile.
  - She protested **very** vehemently.
- An adverb usually tells <u>how</u>, <u>when</u>, <u>where</u>, <u>to what extent</u>, or <u>how often</u>.
- Many adverbs end in <u>-ly</u>.

A. Underline each adverb. Indicate whether the adverb is modifying a verb, an adjective, or another adverb.

_____ **1.** Knute lay quietly on the sofa.

_____ **2.** Carra is a highly competitive individual.

_____ **3.** He walked extremely carefully on the slippery floor.

_____ **4.** When she fell, she landed gently.

_____ **5.** The two-year-old boy gobbled his food very noisily.

_____ **6.** When Laura gets nervous, she speaks quickly.

_____ **7.** David's recollection of the accident was very clouded by the medication.

_____ **8.** The warriors descended from the Trojan Horse stealthily.

_____ **9.** Search and rescue teams looked everywhere for the victim.

_____ **10.** His taste in clothing is excessively expensive.

B. Write three adverbs that could be used to modify each verb.

1. talk   _____   _____   _____

2. lay   _____   _____   _____

3. fought   _____   _____   _____

4. fly   _____   _____   _____

5. argue   _____   _____   _____

6. eat   _____   _____   _____

7. drink   _____   _____   _____

8. leave   _____   _____   _____

9. listen   _____   _____   _____

10. sleep   _____   _____   _____

Comparing with Adverbs

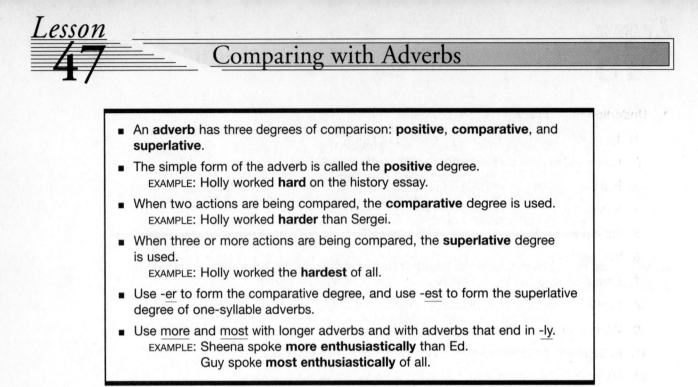

- An **adverb** has three degrees of comparison: **positive**, **comparative**, and **superlative**.
- The simple form of the adverb is called the **positive** degree.
  EXAMPLE: Holly worked **hard** on the history essay.
- When two actions are being compared, the **comparative** degree is used.
  EXAMPLE: Holly worked **harder** than Sergei.
- When three or more actions are being compared, the **superlative** degree is used.
  EXAMPLE: Holly worked the **hardest** of all.
- Use -er to form the comparative degree, and use -est to form the superlative degree of one-syllable adverbs.
- Use more and most with longer adverbs and with adverbs that end in -ly.
  EXAMPLE: Sheena spoke **more enthusiastically** than Ed.
  Guy spoke **most enthusiastically** of all.

A. Write the comparative and superlative form of each adverb.

POSITIVE	COMPARATIVE	SUPERLATIVE
1. long	_____	_____
2. promptly	_____	_____
3. quickly	_____	_____
4. cold	_____	_____
5. energetically	_____	_____
6. fiercely	_____	_____
7. poorly	_____	_____
8. fast	_____	_____

B. Complete each sentence using the correct degree of comparison for each adverb in parentheses. Some of the forms are irregular.

1. (carefully) Does Jonah paint _____ than Eden?

2. (soon) Which of the two e-mails arrived _____ ?

3. (patiently) Who waited _____ , Marta or Justin?

4. (badly) This is the _____ he's ever done on an exam.

5. (frequently) My car breaks down _____ than yours.

6. (well) Lise swims _____ when she competes against others.

Unit 3, Grammar and Usage

A. Underline the correct word.

1. The weather seems (calm, calmly) here at this time of day.

2. Nola's essays are always (careful, carefully) written.

3. Even though our team played (good, well), we didn't get into the finals.

4. Kira is (happy, happily) with her new job in Edmonton.

5. Time passes (slow, slowly) when you are waiting for an announcement.

6. We were (certain, certainly) glad to hear that you'd arrived safely in Churchill Falls.

7. Phoebe tries to do her work (good, well) even when she's tired.

8. I think the horse from your stable will (easy, easily) win the Queen's Plate.

9. We had to shout (loud, loudly) to be heard over the noise of the engines.

10. In September the sun shone (bright, brightly) almost every day.

11. My grandfather sleeps (good, well) after he takes an evening walk.

12. The flu struck very (sudden, suddenly).

13. The barometer measures air pressure (accurate, accurately).

14. The rain fell (steady, steadily) most of the time.

15. The snow looked (beautiful, beautifully) in the morning sunlight.

16. The company always does (good, well) when oil costs are high.

17. Even though they appear to be clumsy, bears can climb (good, well).

18. I was (real, really) excited about going ice fishing on Lake Nipigon.

19. That idea seems (foolish, foolishly) when you consider the risks.

20. My hair seems to grow very (rapid, rapidly) in summer.

B. Write sentences using the words in brackets.

1. (ride, furiously) _____

2. (worked, diligently) _____

3. (seemed, quiet) _____

4. (tread, cautiously) _____

5. (looked, magnificent) _____

6. (wake, quickly) _____

7. (appeared, tired) _____

8. (react, slowly) _____

9. (knock, softly) _____

10. (write, clearly) _____

Prepositions

■ A **preposition** is a word that shows the relationship of a noun or a pronoun to another word in the sentence.

    EXAMPLES: Put the package **on** the table. Place the package **in** the desk.

■ These are some commonly used prepositions:

about	against	at	between	from	near	through	under
above	among	behind	by	in	of	to	upon
across	around	beside	for	into	over	toward	with

A. Draw a line under each preposition or prepositions in the sentences below.

1. Deo greeted his cousin from Japan with a smile and a handshake.

2. They walked toward the baggage area of the airport in Victoria.

3. The two cousins had not seen each other for five years.

4. Deo drove Mariko to the family farm.

5. It was a long ride through beautiful scenery.

6. The farm was located near Courtenay, British Columbia.

7. The cousins walked across the driveway and toward the house.

8. Deo's family gathered around Mariko.

9. Everyone sat on the porch and drank lemonade.

10. Then everyone went into the house and ate dinner.

B. Create sentences using the prepositions in brackets.

1. (across) _____

2. (behind) _____

3. (from) _____

4. (through) _____

5. (toward) _____

6. (over) _____

7. (upon) _____

8. (among) _____

9. (beside) _____

10. (for) _____

Unit 3, Grammar and Usage

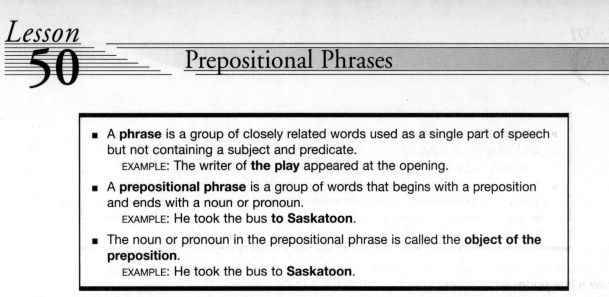

- A **phrase** is a group of closely related words used as a single part of speech but not containing a subject and predicate.
  EXAMPLE: The writer of **the play** appeared at the opening.

- A **prepositional phrase** is a group of words that begins with a preposition and ends with a noun or pronoun.
  EXAMPLE: He took the bus **to Saskatoon**.

- The noun or pronoun in the prepositional phrase is called the **object of the preposition**.
  EXAMPLE: He took the bus to **Saskatoon**.

A. Put parentheses around each prepositional phrase. Then underline each preposition, and circle the object of the preposition.

1. Coal is mined beneath the earth's surface.

2. We are moving to Prince Edward Island.

3. Sonia's family lives on a dairy farm.

4. The caravan travelled around the country.

5. They came upon an abandoned puppy.

6. The chocolate bar was invented in 1910.

7. DNA evidence is now accepted by the courts.

8. Tungsten, a metal, was discovered in the eighteenth century.

9. Roses originally came from Asia.

10. The car rolled into the ditch.

11. Do they always keep the sheep in a pen?

12. The pony jumped over the fence.

13. Tabor lives in Hamilton, Ontario.

14. Samuel de Champlain is called the father of New France.

15. They ate their picnic under a beach umbrella.

16. The lost child was discovered by a search party.

17. The letter dropped behind the desk.

18. They decided to travel across Canada.

19. Solange made her way through the crowd.

20. Grandma was feeling better toward morning.

21. The leopard climbed up the tree.

22. We visited the Alexander Graham Bell Museum in Nova Scotia.

23. The girl raced between parked cars.

24. We spent last summer in the Mackenzie Mountains.

25. Eli decided to have dinner with Karen.

- A prepositional phrase can be used to describe a noun or a pronoun. Then the prepositional phrase is being used as an **adjective** to tell which one, what kind, or how many.
  EXAMPLE: The cat **in the alley** hissed.
- The prepositional phrase <u>in the alley</u> tells **which** cat.
- A prepositional phrase can be used to describe a verb. Then the prepositional phrase is being used as an **adverb** to tell how, where, or when.
  EXAMPLE: Dara ate supper **before the concert**. The prepositional phrase <u>before the concert</u> tells **when** Dara ate supper.

B. Underline each prepositional phrase. Write <u>adj.</u> above phrases used as an adjective, and <u>adv.</u> above phrases used as an adverb.

1. Who discovered potash in Saskatchewan?

2. The diameter of a Sequoia tree trunk can reach three metres.

3. Tula will leave for the cottage in the morning.

4. The capital of Croatia is Zagreb.

5. The girl in the red jacket is my sister.

6. That politician frequently speaks about the homeless.

7. The hockey player from Sweden shows remarkable ability.

8. The airplane flew above the clouds.

9. Send an e-mail to your favourite cousin.

10. The leader of the party promised to cut taxes.

C. Write sentences using the following prepositional phrases.

1. (in the evening) _____

2. (of Canada) _____

3. (behind the couch) _____

4. (near the city) _____

5. (beneath the sea) _____

6. (above the trees) _____

7. (around the corner) _____

8. (over the bridge) _____

9. (among friends) _____

10. (with courage) _____

 Unit 3, Grammar and Usage

> ■ **Participial phrases** begin with a present or past participle and can function as adjectives.
> EXAMPLES: **Reaching for a cookie**, Martin spilled his glass of milk.
> **Damaged beyond repair**, the ship sunk.

A. Underline the participial phrases in the following sentences.

1. My friend, Kamali, devastated by the bad news, slumped down in her chair.

2. We saw the deer standing at the top of the hill.

3. Overcome by smoke, the family staggered out of the burning house.

4. Erik, knowing the secret at last, went to his uncle to ask for advice.

5. Panting from the heat, the dog found a cool spot under a maple tree.

6. Broken by the force of the storm, the window glass shattered on the floor.

> ■ Sometimes participial phrases are misplaced in a sentence so that they modify the wrong word (**misplaced modifier**).
> EXAMPLE: **Misplaced: Grazing peacefully like cattle**, we saw a herd of buffalo. [The participial phrase seems to refer to we.]
> **Revised**: We saw a herd of **buffalo, grazing peacefully like cattle**. [The phrase clearly refers to buffalo.]
> ■ Sometimes the word they modify is implied, but doesn't appear in the sentence (**dangling modifier**). When participial phrases are not clearly related to the words that they modify, confusion can result.
> EXAMPLE: **Dangling: While jogging**, the CD player broke.
> **Revised**: While **jogging, I** broke the CD player.

B. Rewrite the following sentences so that the participial phrase clearly modifies the correct word.

1. Growling loudly, my scarf was being chewed up by the dog.

   _____

2. Tonya saw the sun rise from her favourite bench in the park.

   _____

3. While sleeping outside, the tent blew down.

   _____

4. A graduate of McGill, Andrew's head is bursting with ideas.

   _____

5. A new treatment is being provided for the prevention of snoring in doctors' offices.

   _____

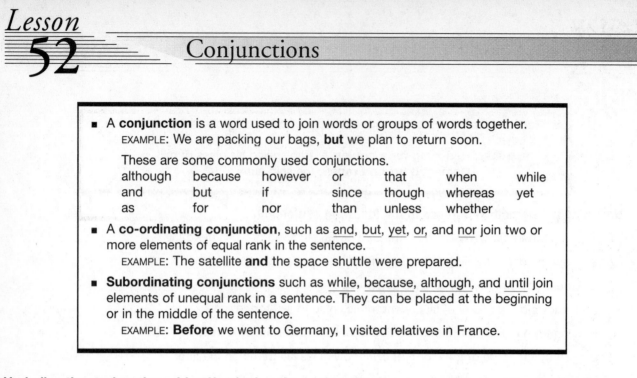

- A **conjunction** is a word used to join words or groups of words together.
  EXAMPLE: We are packing our bags, **but** we plan to return soon.

  These are some commonly used conjunctions.

although	because	however	or	that	when	while
and	but	if	since	though	whereas	yet
as	for	nor	than	unless	whether	

- A **co-ordinating conjunction**, such as <u>and</u>, <u>but</u>, <u>yet</u>, <u>or</u>, and <u>nor</u> join two or more elements of equal rank in the sentence.
  EXAMPLE: The satellite **and** the space shuttle were prepared.

- **Subordinating conjunctions** such as <u>while</u>, <u>because</u>, <u>although</u>, and <u>until</u> join elements of unequal rank in a sentence. They can be placed at the beginning or in the middle of the sentence.
  EXAMPLE: **Before** we went to Germany, I visited relatives in France.

Underline the conjunctions. Identify whether the conjunction is co-ordinating or subordinating by writing <u>C</u> or <u>S</u> above it.

1. It's your decision whether you do it or not.

2. David has battled the disease valiantly since he was a child.

3. I'm not going to do it because I don't like working with Helen.

4. They paid for the renovations though they weren't satisfied with the quality of the work.

5. Both snakes and lizards are cold-blooded animals.

6. My dog Ace comes when he's good and ready.

7. While the sheep grazed, the border collies remained alert.

8. Although Mr. Singh retired from teaching in 1995, he still keeps in touch with his students.

9. Jess won't get into the computer animation program unless she has a good portfolio.

10. We're visiting Nova Scotia or New Brunswick next summer.

11. Because we are late, we won't stop to talk.

12. The climbers were exhausted, yet they continued on.

13. If I pass my swimming test, I will be qualified to instruct.

14. When summer arrives, Bianca plans to go camping.

15. Does that writer want fame or fortune?

> - The adverbs <u>not</u>, <u>never</u>, <u>hardly</u>, <u>scarcely</u>, <u>seldom</u>, <u>none</u>, and <u>nothing</u> should not be used with a negative verb. One clause cannot properly contain two negatives.
>   EXAMPLES: There **wasn't anything** left in the cupboard. (**Correct**)
>   There **wasn't nothing** left in the cupboard. (**Incorrect**)

A. Underline the correct word.

1. I don't know (any, none) of the people in this room.

2. Rafaela couldn't do (anything, nothing) about changing the time of that appointment.

3. We didn't have (any, no) milk or butter in the fridge.

4. There isn't (any, no) paper left in this printer.

5. Elsa hasn't said (anything, nothing) about the surprise party.

6. Hardly (anything, nothing) makes her angry.

7. There aren't (any, no) buses leaving for Ottawa tonight.

8. There wasn't (anybody, nobody) in the information kiosk.

9. I haven't solved (any, none) of my math problems yet.

10. I haven't done (anything, nothing) to offend Greg.

11. Hasn't he put (any, none) of the tomatoes in the salad?

12. They didn't have (any, no) time to waste.

13. There isn't (anybody, nobody) that Marcia can trust.

14. The maple trees don't have (any, no) protection from strong winds.

15. The suspect insisted that he hadn't done (anything, nothing) wrong.

B. Rewrite the following paragraph, correcting all the double negatives.

I like going shopping, but I don't do no shopping on Saturdays. There isn't nothing I need badly enough to face crowded shopping malls. My friends say I never go nowhere on the weekend. I don't care if I don't see nobody. It's easier to stay home and relax.

A. Write the part of speech above each underlined word. Use the abbreviations given in the box.

1. A light wind blew across the desert.

2. What a wonderful treat!

3. The heavy fog gradually lifted in the morning.

4. Remy and I are showing pictures of the mountains that we saw on our trip.

5. Is the capital of your province built on a river?

6. Those trees are gigantic.

7. Everyone left the room very quickly and hurried outside.

8. Please put this extremely valuable necklace very carefully in the vault.

9. The angry crowd waited for the corrupt politician to speak.

10. Strange circles of grey stone appeared in this ploughed field.

n.	noun
pron.	pronoun
v.	verb
adj.	adjective
adv.	adverb
prep.	preposition
conj.	conjunction

B. Write the plural form or the possessive form of the noun in parentheses.

1. (brush) The paint _____ need to be cleaned.

2. (cry) The _____ echoed throughout the valley.

3. (hero) All of the _____ honours did not change his humility.

4. (pony) The _____ mane is matted with burrs.

5. (fox) The _____ hole is deep in the woods.

C. Circle the correct verb.

1. Bill Gates has (gave, given) computers to many libraries.

2. Was it the telephone or the doorbell that (rang, rung)?

3. Our guest (come, came) before dinner.

4. Yoko has (know, known) Peter for eight months.

5. We wanted to (drive, driven) from Winnipeg to Regina in one day.

6. Haven't you (ate, eaten) enough chocolate for one day?

7. The birds have (gone, went) to Mexico for the winter.

8. Matt (doesn't, don't) like to be late for class.

9. Helga (did, done) all her homework before leaving for the party.

10. One of the actors (was, were) injured in a train accident.

D. Rewrite each sentence, using the active voice.

1. The child was bitten by a dog.

_____

2. I was bored by the lesson.

_____

3. The map was misplaced by the driver.

_____

E. Underline the pronoun in parentheses that agrees with the antecedent. Circle the antecedent.

1. Aaron and Alice helped Howie because (he, they) had been sick for a week.
2. The student had to leave (her, its) school when the power failed.
3. Bob and André brought the posters to (them, their) campaign office.
4. My sister collected baskets on (her, their) trip to Mexico.
5. The charity collected donations and gave (it, them) to the homeless.

F. Underline the adjectives and the adverbs. Write adj. above the adjectives and adv. above the adverbs.

1. The hungry colt munched the fresh grass steadily.
2. The blue lake seemed very calm before the storm erupted suddenly and violently.
3. Athena was extremely upset about the low mark she received on the geography test.
4. The frightened puppy quivered uncontrollably.
5. A babbling brook ran quite swiftly into the river.

G. Underline each prepositional phrase. Write adj. above phrases used as adjectives, and adv. above phrases used as adverbs.

1. The ship sailed from Halifax Harbour.
2. The gymnast from Kamloops will be going to the Olympics.
3. Why are we leaving for the station before dawn?
4. Pitch the tent near the river.
5. The star of that TV show does not give interviews.

H. Underline the prepositions and conjunctions. Write prep. above the prepositions and conj. above the conjunctions.

1. Wapi wanted to go to the lake, but he realized that the beach is near a power dam.
2. Because I'm tired, I will rest for ten minutes under a tree.
3. Unless we reach port before dark, the winds will be against us.
4. Should we go to the park or walk near the river?
5. When Dagmar arrives in the morning, we will meet.

Using What You've Learned

A. Read the following paragraphs.

The first people who came to Canada arrived during the last Ice Age, which began about 80 000 years ago and ended about 12 000 years ago. These people were hunters who crossed from Asia by a land bridge that is now submerged beneath the Bering Sea. Although archaeologists debate when the earliest human might have settled in Canada, artifacts at least 12 000 to 17 000 years old have been found at the Bluefish Caves in the Yukon.

These people eventually moved to other parts of Canada. Some fished and hunted, but others, such as the Eastern Woodland people, lived by farming. Trading patterns, arts and crafts, languages, religious beliefs, laws, and government were very well developed by the First Nations peoples before explorers arrived from Europe.

B. Write two plural nouns from the paragraph above.

_____   _____

C. Write two passive verbs.

_____   _____

D. Write four relative pronouns and their antecedents.

1. _____   _____   3. _____   _____

2. _____   _____   4. _____   _____

E. Write two adjectives.

_____   _____

F. Write two adverbs.

_____   _____

G. Write three prepositional phrases.

1. _____

2. _____

3. _____

H. Write two conjunctions.

_____   _____

72   © 2000 Gage Educational Publishing Company   **Unit 3, Grammar and Usage**

I. Read the following paragraphs.

Rivers are one of the most important physical features. Rivers have cut channels between mountains, creating deep gorges. They have also flooded huge areas of land. Even more importantly, rivers can provide food, fresh water, and transportation.

The St. Lawrence River affected the settlement of Canada. Following the St. Lawrence, early settlers from Europe were able to reach the Great Lakes system and access Canada's interior. These settlers worked with determination to build settlements for themselves and for generations to come. Many large Canadian cities, including Winnipeg, Montréal, and Vancouver, are located on rivers. Rivers play a vital role that is hardly never recognized.

J. Write a plural noun, a proper noun, a concrete noun, and an abstract noun.

1. _____ 3. _____

2. _____ 4. _____

K. Write two pronouns and their antecedents.

1. _____ _____ 2. _____ _____

L. Write one superlative adjective. _____

M. Write one comparative adverb. _____

N. Write two prepositional phrases that are used as adjectives.

_____

_____

O. Write two prepositional phrases that are used as adverbs.

_____

_____

P. Write two participial phrases.

_____

_____

Q. Write a double negative.

_____

- **Capitalize** the first word of a sentence and of each line of poetry.
  EXAMPLES: Taro recited a poem. The first two lines follow.
  They wandered through the hills and streams
  In search of their forgotten dreams.

- Capitalize the first word of a direct quotation.
  EXAMPLE: Juan said, "Let's find a place to eat."

- Capitalize the first, last, and all important words in the titles of books, poems, stories, and songs.
  EXAMPLES: *The Stone Angel*; "Shooting the Sun"

A. Circle each letter that should be capitalized. Write the capital letter above it.

1. Rafaela asked, "what time does the bus leave?"

2. calixa lavallée wrote the music for "o canada."

3. joni mitchell, the writer of "both sides, now," was born in fort macleod, alberta.

4. mac asked, "when do you plan to start university?"

5. who wrote the poems "a farewell" and "the solitary reaper"?

6. what famous canadian said, "the medium is the message"?

- Capitalize all **proper nouns**.
  EXAMPLES: Kim Stockwood, Father, Bloor Street, India, Nova Scotia, Laurentian Mountains, Thanksgiving, May, Museum of Civilization, *Bluenose*.

- Capitalize all **proper adjectives**. A proper adjective is an adjective that is made from a proper noun.
  EXAMPLES: the Russian language, Thai food, American tourists

B. Circle each letter that should be capitalized. Write the capital letter above it.

1. Emile, does your aunt live in edmonton, alberta, or prince albert, saskatchewan?

2. The ottawa river forms a boundary between ontario and québec.

3. *who has seen the wind* and *jake and the kid* were written by w.o. mitchell.

4. french explorers discovered the st. lawrence river before franklin searched for the northwest passage.

5. The founder of the canadian red cross was george sterling ryerson.

6. Tropical forests are found in every continent except europe and antarctica.

> - Capitalize a person's title when it comes before a name.
>   EXAMPLES: Mayor Lastman, Doctor Robitaille, Professor Chan
> - Capitalize abbreviations of titles.
>   EXAMPLES: Ms. C. Cohen, Dr. Katsak, Gen. Milne

C. Circle each letter that should be capitalized. Write the capital letter above it.

1. How long have you been consulting dr. mehta?

2. Our class invited reverend davies to speak at graduation.

3. dr. wilder penfield of montréal developed a surgical cure for some types of epilepsy.

4. When do you expect mr. and mrs. slezak to return?

5. Do you think premier klein will win re-election?

6. It will be a close race unless mayor ricci gains more support.

7. When is ms. awa scheduled to begin her law degree?

> - Capitalize abbreviations of days and months, parts of addresses, and titles of members of the armed forces. Also capitalize all letters in the abbreviations of provinces.
>   EXAMPLES: Wed.; Dec.; 403 S. Oxford St.; Maj. Sally T. Lange; Markham, ON; L3R 1E5

D. Circle each letter that should be capitalized. Write the capital letter above it.

1. westwood school science fair
   fri., jan. 9, 10 A.M.
   142 n. maple blvd.

2. souris sea festival
   july 26–28
   r.r. 1
   souris, pe c0a 2b0

3. autumn fest
   october 2 and 3
   11 A.M.–10 P.M.
   84 roxborough st.

4. barbara wong
   150 shore rd.
   nanaimo, bc v9r 6v8

5. captain t.m. kelley
   c/o flying gull
   p.o. box 3264
   st. john's, nf a1e 6b4

6. dr. martha pym
   stevens memorial hospital
   33 drummond street
   vegreville, alberta t9c 1t9

> - Use a **period** at the end of a declarative sentence.
>   EXAMPLE: People need oxygen to live.
>
> - Use a **question mark** at the end of an interrogative sentence.
>   EXAMPLE: How much oxygen do people need?
>
> - Use an **exclamation mark** at the end of an exclamatory sentence.
>   EXAMPLE: We're running out of oxygen!

A. Use a period or question mark to end each sentence below.

1. Doesn't Apphia's mother now live in Whitehorse _____

2. "The Leaving" is a well-known short story _____

3. Isn't that the same shirt you wore yesterday, Garth _____

4. We saw three plays at Stratford, didn't we _____

5. Show some spirit _____

6. The greatest library in ancient times was in Alexandria, Egypt _____

7. Who in that organization can be trusted _____

8. Will Ms. Kressman start interviewing applicants next Monday _____

9. Her sister has moved to Brandon, Manitoba _____

10. Hurry up or we'll be late _____

11. The Toronto Maple Leafs left Maple Leaf Gardens in 1999 _____

12. I've fed the cat, walked the dog, and watered the plants _____

13. Did World War I begin on August 4, 1914 _____

14. Stand straight and don't slouch _____

15. Is Grenoble in France or Switzerland _____

B. Add the correct punctuation where needed in the paragraphs below.

You are part of the crew of a space laboratory orbiting the sun _____ Your mission will keep you and the rest of the crew in space for at least ten years _____ How will you survive _____

Everything you need for life support is on board: food, water, oxygen, heat, and light. Does it sound simple _____ But there's one more issue to consider _____ When your supplies run out, they can't be replaced _____ Wouldn't you want to be careful about using your supplies _____ Your existence could depend on it _____

This spaceship is Planet Earth _____ The crew is all of us living on Earth _____ How many of our resources are limited and non-renewable _____ When they're used up, they can't be replaced _____ Shouldn't we be careful about how we utilize those precious resources _____ Our lives really do depend on them _____

Commas

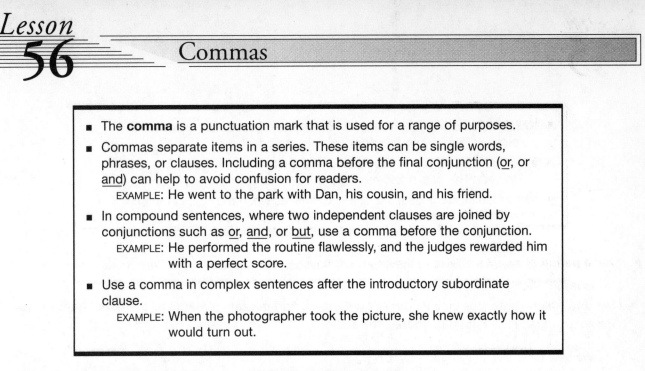

- The **comma** is a punctuation mark that is used for a range of purposes.

- Commas separate items in a series. These items can be single words, phrases, or clauses. Including a comma before the final conjunction (<u>or</u>, or <u>and</u>) can help to avoid confusion for readers.
  EXAMPLE: He went to the park with Dan, his cousin, and his friend.

- In compound sentences, where two independent clauses are joined by conjunctions such as <u>or</u>, <u>and</u>, or <u>but</u>, use a comma before the conjunction.
  EXAMPLE: He performed the routine flawlessly, and the judges rewarded him with a perfect score.

- Use a comma in complex sentences after the introductory subordinate clause.
  EXAMPLE: When the photographer took the picture, she knew exactly how it would turn out.

Correct these sentences by adding commas in the appropriate places.

1. The player approached the batter's box took a few swings and hit the ball.

2. Dierdre was late but she came to the concert anyway.

3. In case of emergency break the glass.

4. She is chief executive officer sales manager and buyer for the company.

5. He can entertain us with his beautiful tenor voice or he can play the harp.

6. When you go to the 1960s dance be sure to wear some flowers in your hair.

7. Do you want fries fish sticks or onion rings with your order?

8. This is his first official visit to Nunavut and I'm sure it will be the first of many.

9. I have seen waves at Long Beach and I have seen cormorants on the Newfoundland cliffs.

10. The provinces competing in the tournament include Alberta Saskatchewan and Manitoba.

11. In my brief time at the school he has been reprimanded eight times.

12. It's not my role to report absences and it's not your role to make judgments.

13. I have to renew my passport book a flight and obtain an international driver's licence.

14. If I don't get my cheque in time I will lose a great opportunity and that could ruin my life.

15. That night when all was ready we made coffee.

16. My sister studied physics engineering and medicine.

17. We bought a computer four years ago but it's already obsolete.

18. If you go to the store buy a litre of milk.

19. Do you want to bake cookies watch a video or fix your bike?

20. France Italy Germany and Spain are popular tourist destinations.

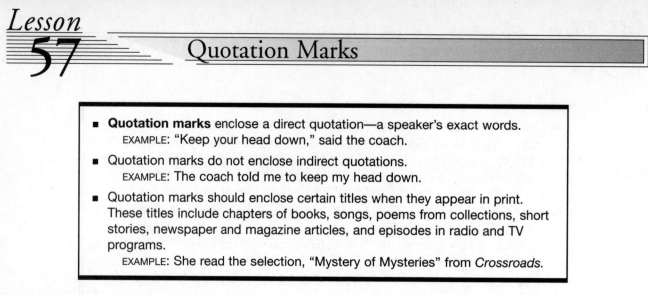

- **Quotation marks** enclose a direct quotation—a speaker's exact words.
  EXAMPLE: "Keep your head down," said the coach.
- Quotation marks do not enclose indirect quotations.
  EXAMPLE: The coach told me to keep my head down.
- Quotation marks should enclose certain titles when they appear in print. These titles include chapters of books, songs, poems from collections, short stories, newspaper and magazine articles, and episodes in radio and TV programs.
  EXAMPLE: She read the selection, "Mystery of Mysteries" from *Crossroads*.

A. Identify which sentences include direct quotations. Add quotation marks to the direct quotations. Be sure to place the quotation marks correctly.

1. She said, I will not live forever.

2. The teacher told me to bring the book back to the library.

3. Let them go free, chorused the crowd.

4. He asked me to go to the game.

5. Tell me something I'll never forget, he said.

6. We had heard him say a million times, A bird in the hand is worth two in the bush.

7. Lunch is ready. Come and get it! he called.

8. Melody responded, I find the human brain extremely fascinating.

9. Her exact words were, Bake the cake before tomorrow morning.

10. Well, Mr. Fulghum, what do you think?

B. Use quotation marks as required with the titles below.

1. The information you want is in Chapter 3, The War Years.

2. Candle in the Wind by Elton John is a very moving song.

3. I very much enjoyed Felice Holman's poem, Who Am I?

4. I obtained the information for my report in an article from *Elm Street* called Cultivating Change.

5. Artichoke Pie is tonight's *Black Harbour* episode.

6. Never Too Late is my favourite story from that collection.

7. Did you read Movies to Remember in Saturday's *Globe and Mail*?

8. Joseph Bruchac wrote a poem called Birdfoot's Grandpa.

9. I couldn't understand Chapter 6, Inertia and Motion.

10. My parents were listening to a song called Yesterday.

Punctuating Dialogue

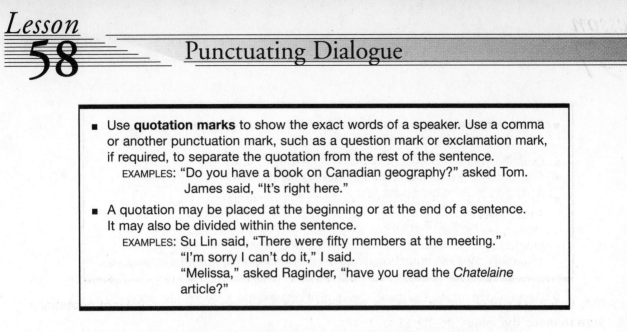

- Use **quotation marks** to show the exact words of a speaker. Use a comma or another punctuation mark, such as a question mark or exclamation mark, if required, to separate the quotation from the rest of the sentence.

  EXAMPLES: "Do you have a book on Canadian geography?" asked Tom.
  James said, "It's right here."

- A quotation may be placed at the beginning or at the end of a sentence. It may also be divided within the sentence.

  EXAMPLES: Su Lin said, "There were fifty members at the meeting."
  "I'm sorry I can't do it," I said.
  "Melissa," asked Raginder, "have you read the *Chatelaine* article?"

A. Add quotation marks and other necessary punctuation in the sentences below.

1. Marnie, did you ever play hockey asked Shania.

2. Shen asked Why didn't you come to the interview

3. Darwin said Yuri thank you for the gift

4. When do we start our canoe trip in Algonquin Park asked Michel.

5. The guest said You don't know how happy I am to be in your house.

6. My sister said Kelly brought those beautiful pots from Hornby Island.

7. I'm going to plant the broccoli said Ramiro as soon as I return home.

8. What's all the fuss about Carl wanted to know.

9. Do you like chocolate asked Tam.

10. I will leave he announced as soon as I find out the truth.

11. Ali said I will not forget your kindness.

12. How far is it to Moose Jaw the stranger wanted to know.

13. Judge Livingstone stated There will be a short recess.

B. The following sentences come from a short story called "G. Trueheart, Man's Best Friend." Use your editing skills to add missing quotation marks, and to correct the placement of punctuation where necessary.

1. Rusty has to stay to chase pheasants", his mother said.

2. "What if I meet a cougar" Tom said.

3. The kids asked Tom ",What's she good for

4. Boy, oh, boy!," a kid said I wouldn't be seen with her for two dollars a week

5. She's a city dog" Tom said.

6. Aunt Prudence said ", Now you should know how much she loves you, Tommy.

7. Yah Tommy said

Apostrophes

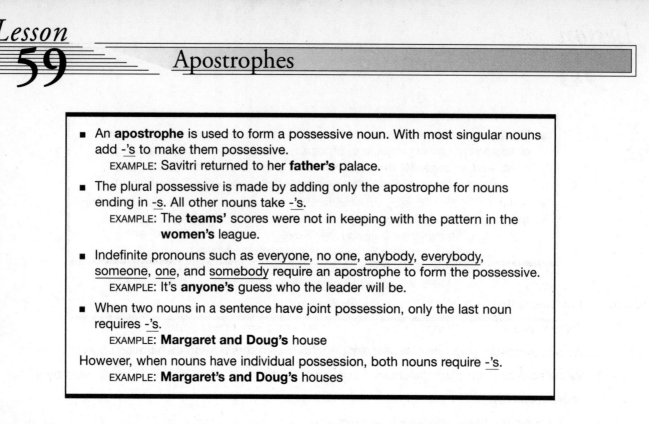

- An **apostrophe** is used to form a possessive noun. With most singular nouns add -'s to make them possessive.
  EXAMPLE: Savitri returned to her **father's** palace.

- The plural possessive is made by adding only the apostrophe for nouns ending in -s. All other nouns take -'s.
  EXAMPLE: The **teams'** scores were not in keeping with the pattern in the **women's** league.

- Indefinite pronouns such as everyone, no one, anybody, everybody, someone, one, and somebody require an apostrophe to form the possessive.
  EXAMPLE: It's **anyone's** guess who the leader will be.

- When two nouns in a sentence have joint possession, only the last noun requires -'s.
  EXAMPLE: **Margaret and Doug's** house

However, when nouns have individual possession, both nouns require -'s.
  EXAMPLE: **Margaret's and Doug's** houses

After each sentence below, write the word in which an apostrophe has been left out. Add the apostrophe where needed.

1. Many players uniforms are red. _____

2. Those dogs played with the babys shoe. _____

3. Sun Lung isn't coming to the librarys opening with us. _____

4. The captains ship was one of the newest. _____

5. Mens coats are sold in the new store. _____

6. All that maple trees leaves are coming down. _____

7. Is someones lost child your concern? _____

8. Dans and Melissas marks were the last ones to be called out. _____

9. Everyones case will be handled individually. _____

10. In a history book, he read that the Beatles first tour of North America was a great success.

   _____

11. My mothers business involves e-commerce. _____

12. The girls teams entered the tournament. _____

- Use a **dash** to set off words that interrupt the main thought of a sentence, or to show a sudden change of thought.
  EXAMPLE: The robber ran right by me—I could see his sweaty face—and disappeared down the alley.

- A dash can also be used to introduce information or an explanation. It can be used to mean "in other words" or "that is."
  EXAMPLE: There's only one way you'll ever get me to jump out of an airplane—make sure it never leaves the ground.

Add dashes where they are needed in the sentences below.

1. There was a loud thud what a surprise from the back of the bowling alley.

2. We all turned around Marci even jumped up to see what was making the strange sound.

3. Paul Devereaux you know the person I mean told me the football game would be decided by a single touchdown.

4. I thought about taking another route the one through southern Manitoba.

5. I'd love to see *Love's Labours Lost* again perhaps in August and bring Ravi.

6. There's only one way to ride that bull take out millions of dollars in accident insurance.

7. Our plane left for Angola at long last around 2:45 P.M.

8. In the story Victor had one option marry the Count's stepsister.

9. The conclusion to the mystery I don't mind saying is somewhat elementary.

10. We ended up not going to the movie but that's another story.

11. Horror movies I'm afraid to say are not my favourite form of entertainment.

12. The band leader and everyone else in her group should be congratulated.

13. It was the part of the play if you can believe it that was meant to add suspense.

14. This building and every one on the street like it must be demolished.

15. This man's the culprit I recognize his face.

16. The game much to our annoyance has been postponed until May 1.

17. We finally arrived at the restaurant after the door was locked.

18. I know I can do it just give me a chance!

19. We want to travel in Canada maybe to the Maritimes later this summer.

20. My grandparents and others of their generation love to have visits with young people.

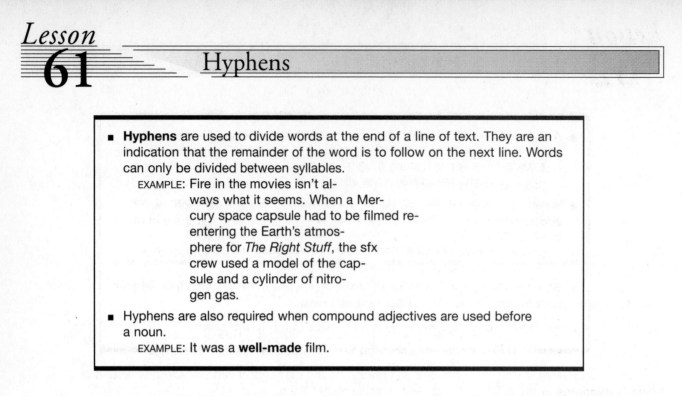

- **Hyphens** are used to divide words at the end of a line of text. They are an indication that the remainder of the word is to follow on the next line. Words can only be divided between syllables.

  EXAMPLE: Fire in the movies isn't always what it seems. When a Mer-
  cury space capsule had to be filmed re-
  entering the Earth's atmos-
  phere for *The Right Stuff*, the sfx
  crew used a model of the capsule and a cylinder of nitro-
  gen gas.

- Hyphens are also required when compound adjectives are used before a noun.

  EXAMPLE: It was a **well-made** film.

A. Indicate where you would hyphenate these words if they appeared at the end of a line. Note that in some words, there are a number of possibilities. The first one is done for you. Use a dictionary to check your word divisions.

1. township   town-ship _____

2. business _____

3. separate _____

4. insinuation _____

5. dependable _____

6. planning _____

7. leathery _____

8. continue _____

9. oxygen _____

10. graduation _____

11. clerical _____

12. invincible _____

13. assessing _____

14. cushion _____

B. Rewrite the following phrases inserting the hyphen where it belongs.

1. a silver grey skirt _____

2. a problem solving strategy _____

3. a city owned park _____

4. a six centimetre high model _____

5. a life or death situation _____

6. a poverty stricken community _____

Lesson 62

Semicolons

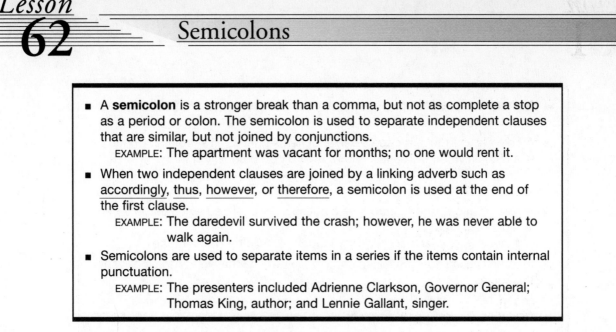

- A **semicolon** is a stronger break than a comma, but not as complete a stop as a period or colon. The semicolon is used to separate independent clauses that are similar, but not joined by conjunctions.
  - EXAMPLE: The apartment was vacant for months; no one would rent it.
- When two independent clauses are joined by a linking adverb such as <u>accordingly</u>, <u>thus</u>, <u>however</u>, or <u>therefore</u>, a semicolon is used at the end of the first clause.
  - EXAMPLE: The daredevil survived the crash; however, he was never able to walk again.
- Semicolons are used to separate items in a series if the items contain internal punctuation.
  - EXAMPLE: The presenters included Adrienne Clarkson, Governor General; Thomas King, author; and Lennie Gallant, singer.

Place semicolons in the correct places in the sentences below.

1. The tornado spun across the prairie her barn was swept away.

2. The conference ends on Sunday thus, we can return to work for Monday.

3. Ahmed told me not to stay in a hotel he suggested, instead, that I stay with his parents.

4. We ordered five cartons of fax paper six unlined, yellow pads and assorted highlighters in shades of yellow, blue, and orange.

5. We had hoped to complete the journey on foot however, the bad weather prevented us from completing the project.

6. In the Blue Jays game there were three hits, two runs, and one error in the first inning five hits, one run, and no errors in the second inning no hits, no runs, and no errors in the third.

7. He was soaked his whole body was shivering.

8. I asked everyone at the party to avoid discussions about politics I was nervous about a fight breaking out.

9. The company showed a great profit accordingly, the dividends will be passed on to shareholders.

10. Aunt Jessica looked all over for the right birthday present she finally found what she wanted.

11. They were lost in the storm the car was stuck in a deep drift.

12. Technology is changing therefore we must adapt.

13. You are very talented however, talent is sometimes not enough.

14. Conferences were held in London, Ontario, on May 6, 1998 in Red Deer, Alberta, on June 8, 1999 and in Moncton, New Brunswick, on July 12, 2000.

15. It was a hectic week we were extremely busy.

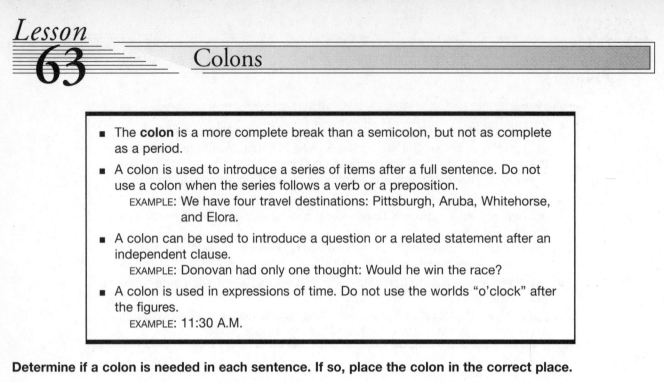

- The **colon** is a more complete break than a semicolon, but not as complete as a period.

- A colon is used to introduce a series of items after a full sentence. Do not use a colon when the series follows a verb or a preposition.
  EXAMPLE: We have four travel destinations: Pittsburgh, Aruba, Whitehorse, and Elora.

- A colon can be used to introduce a question or a related statement after an independent clause.
  EXAMPLE: Donovan had only one thought: Would he win the race?

- A colon is used in expressions of time. Do not use the worlds "o'clock" after the figures.
  EXAMPLE: 11:30 A.M.

Determine if a colon is needed in each sentence. If so, place the colon in the correct place.

1. Our five travel destinations are Winnipeg, Niagara Falls, Canada's Wonderland, Montréal, and Ottawa.

2. At the antique auction, my aunt was interested in five items a four-poster bed, a hope chest, a hat rack, a brass bedpan, and a vanity mirror.

3. I know the answer reverse the independent and the subordinate clauses.

4. The Stampeder tickets were distributed as follows fifty tickets for our school, thirty to a school north of the city, and twenty for a school from a rural area.

5. At the end of the day, there's only one person who will put up with his antics his mother.

6. She worked all through her twenties to become a lawyer she achieved her goal.

7. The members of the sales force were assigned to cover different areas Western, Eastern, and Central Canada.

8. You will need the following items for the examination a protractor, a pencil, a calculator, and a periodic table.

9. His solution to the problem bring a socket wrench.

10. Her plane will arrive in Victoria at 1 45 P.M. on Friday.

11. Lenny prepared a dessert feast apple pie, cheesecake, date squares, butter tarts, and chocolate brownies.

12. The train was scheduled to depart at 4 00, but it didn't leave the station until 5 15.

13. The Olympic athlete had a lofty goal to bring honour to her country.

14. Kids at the camp were from British Columbia, Manitoba, Nova Scotia, and New Brunswick.

15. Garth suddenly remembered his father's statement be home by 11 00.

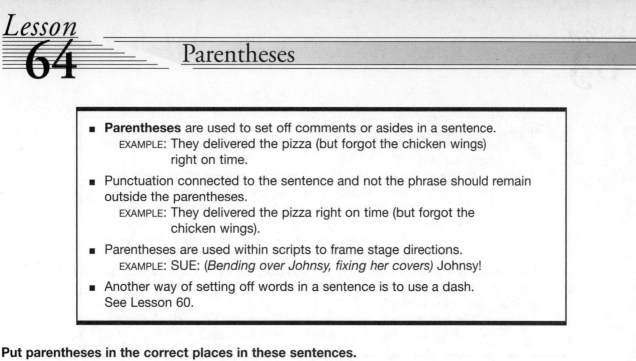

- **Parentheses** are used to set off comments or asides in a sentence.
    EXAMPLE: They delivered the pizza (but forgot the chicken wings) right on time.
- Punctuation connected to the sentence and not the phrase should remain outside the parentheses.
    EXAMPLE: They delivered the pizza right on time (but forgot the chicken wings).
- Parentheses are used within scripts to frame stage directions.
    EXAMPLE: SUE: (*Bending over Johnsy, fixing her covers*) Johnsy!
- Another way of setting off words in a sentence is to use a dash. See Lesson 60.

Put parentheses in the correct places in these sentences.

1. The park is always crowded except in black fly season in the spring and summer.

2. DOCTOR: *As they walk to the door* She's a very sick girl.

3. We provide a complete list of stores see the Appendix.

4. I called Dennis Monday night or was it Tuesday to give him the message.

5. BEN: *Looks* Of course I can see them. Why do you ask?

6. After listing her hypothesis part of the scientific inquiry process, she wrote out her procedures, results, and conclusions.

7. MS. NAMIS: I didn't want you to come here. Nadia didn't want you to come here. *Knock at the door*

8. All of us except Shannon Shannon is always optimistic thought it was going to rain.

9. They lived happily ever after and so did the cat.

10. FERRIS: *Falling to the floor* This time you've gone too far. *Eyes close*

11. MARINA: *Grinning* What do you think of my invention now?

12. That classic novel abridged version has gone out of print.

13. I will pick up the concert tickets soon tomorrow morning.

14. RAOUL: Too bad you didn't get here sooner. *Shakes his head*

15. Tell me what happened if you can remember.

16. Credit cards or cash if you have it will be accepted.

17. MILA: *Stepping forward* I volunteer to go.

18. These people and others like them deserve to have jobs.

19. MAYOR: Our city is the best in the world. *Waits for applause*

20. My ancestors on both sides of the family came from China.

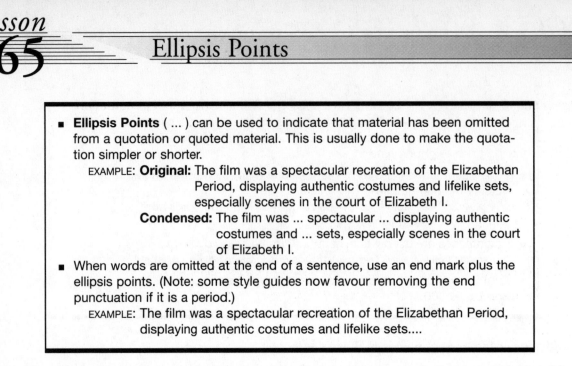

- **Ellipsis Points** (...) can be used to indicate that material has been omitted from a quotation or quoted material. This is usually done to make the quotation simpler or shorter.

    EXAMPLE: **Original:** The film was a spectacular recreation of the Elizabethan Period, displaying authentic costumes and lifelike sets, especially scenes in the court of Elizabeth I.

    Condensed: The film was ... spectacular ... displaying authentic costumes and ... sets, especially scenes in the court of Elizabeth I.

- When words are omitted at the end of a sentence, use an end mark plus the ellipsis points. (Note: some style guides now favour removing the end punctuation if it is a period.)

    EXAMPLE: The film was a spectacular recreation of the Elizabethan Period, displaying authentic costumes and lifelike sets....

Rewrite the following sentences using ellipsis points to show that the underlined material has been omitted. Note how the meaning of the quotation can change.

1. This film is Elvis Presley's best film <u>as far as musical sequences go</u>, but it is still burdened by a sappy plot.

    _____

2. The movie is an engaging <u>screwball musical</u> comedy about a baseball player who tries to win the affection of a <u>bright and lively</u> singing star.

    _____

    _____

3. You will enjoy this splendid entertainment about <u>a group of</u> people in a retirement home who find <u>that they believe</u> in the fountain of youth.

    _____

    _____

4. Jason King stars as a government investigator sent to uncover a security leak <u>that led to the destruction of the space laboratory.</u>

    _____

5. *The Eggplant from New York City* is a badly written and acted film <u>which camouflages a good idea.</u>

    _____

6. The circus clowns performed a <u>rollicking, original</u> show that cheered <u>and uplifted the imagination and</u> the heart.

    _____

A. Circle each letter that should be capitalized. Then add the correct end punctuation.

1. dr. alexandra potvin practises dentistry in shelburne, nova scotia ____

2. is wednesday, march 3, too early for our trip to the zoo ____

3. adrienne clarkson, canada's governor general, is in residence at rideau hall ____

4. we can't possibly finish the job by friday ____

5. does air canada offer flights to istanbul, turkey ____

6. last november we read "borders," a short story by thomas king ____

7. mr. landsborough taught at st. francis school in lethbridge, alberta ____

8. who is the author of "the road not taken" ____

9. duck or you'll be hit ____

10. did you see the review of *grey owl* in *maclean's* ____

B. Add commas where needed in the sentences below.

1. After Joseph got out of high school he started an apprenticeship.

2. They brought pizza chips and pop to the farewell party.

3. Hamidi is returning home in April but not before the baseball season opens.

4. I saw the accident ran for help and called 911 on the phone.

5. Although she is only sixteen she is mature and capable.

6. Therese received a watch a school ring and an airline ticket for her birthday.

7. Quentin spoke with enthusiasm and the crowd loved it.

8. We bought nails paint and sandpaper at the hardware store.

9. Because of the storm we did not go hiking.

10. Caroline was annoyed but she did not leave the gathering.

C. Add commas and quotation marks where needed in the sentences below.

1. Never underestimate your abilities counselled the guest speaker.

2. The Jade Peony is a short story by Wayson Choy.

3. I'm tired of peanut butter whined Alison but I don't have time to shop.

4. Ahmed replied Why don't we all go to the game?

5. Dover Beach is a famous poem from the nineteenth century.

6. It's not my fault replied Gordon and I won't take responsibility.

7. Did you see the article called PM Overpowers Critics in today's *Globe and Mail*?

8. Jenna answered We must work together if we want to win.

9. Please return my phone calls requested Marilyn.

10. Turn to Chapter 8 Managing Personal Finances.

D. Insert apostrophes, hyphens, semicolons, and colons where needed in the sentences below.

1. Jackies sister brought the following equipment tent, camp stove, flashlight, and bug spray.

2. MASHA I've told you these things many times before. (*Turning her back to the audience*)

3. The womens team hired a well known caterer to prepare the barbecue at Alicias house.

4. Amayas brother will meet me at 9 30 on Thursday at Bartons Café.

5. Note a condensed version of one critics remarks on *Pygmalion* This is a well cast production with inspired costumes … amusing moments … thoroughly entertaining.

6. It's everyones responsibility to protect government owned wetlands.

7. The temperature rose quickly several avalanches developed near the mountains peak.

8. The teachers meeting will start at 8 00 speakers will begin at 8 30.

E. Punctuate the letter below. Circle each letter that should be capitalized.

44 gerrard st. w.

toronto, ON

m5g 2k2

may 5, 2000

Dear ms. markowski:

thank you for offering me the computer technicians position with your company____ you mentioned that my responsibilities would be the following fixing computers serving customers and installing software ____ theres one issue we did not discuss ____ when do i start ____ i can be available with a weeks notice ____ call me any time after 5 00 or even sooner if you have need of me ____ although i am still working in my present job my manager knows i am going through a career changing ____ process ____

i hope to hear from you soon

Yours sincerely,

susana marinelli

A. Add punctuation where needed in the paragraphs below. Circle each letter that should be capitalized.

have you ever heard the story called "water, moon and sun" ____ long ago Sun and Moon got married and they were very happy for a while ____ the time came when they wanted to see their friends again and their very best friend was called water____ what about paying us a visit ____ sun called to water across earth ____ its been a long time since we saw you ____ water asked can I bring my friends ____ of course answered sun ____

water set off to visit sun and moon ____ with him went many sardines whales sharks fish and lobsters____ water swirled into the village and he soon covered the floor of his friends home ____ sun and moon its wonderful to see you again said water ____ soon water and the creatures he had brought filled the whole village____ im leaving wept moon ____ she took a leap into the sky and sun followed her ____ water was left down below with his fishy friends____

thats why there are lakes rivers and seas all over the world and why the sun and moon shine down on them from up above ____

B. Write a sentence to illustrate each use of punctuation.

1. Comma

_____

2. Quotation Marks

_____

3. Apostrophe

_____

4. Dash

_____

5. Hyphen

_____

6. Semicolon

_____

7. Colon

_____

8. Parentheses

_____

9. Ellipsis Points

_____

C. Rewrite the story below. Be sure to use capital letters and punctuation marks where they are needed.

sir walter scott one of the worlds greatest storytellers was born in edinburgh, scotland, on august 15, 1771 ____ walter had an illness just before he was two years old that left him lame for the rest of his life ____ his parents were worried so they sent him to his grandparents farm in sandy knowe ____ they thought the country air would do him good ____

walters parents were right ____ he was quite healthy by the time he was six years old ____ he was happy, too ____ walter loved listening to his grandfather tell stories about scotland ____ the stories stirred his imagination ____ he began to read fairy tales travel books and history books ____ it was these early stories that laid the groundwork for Scotts later interest in writing stories ____ his most famous book *Ivanhoe* has been read by people around the world ____

Writing Sentences

- Every sentence has a base consisting of a simple subject and a simple predicate.

    EXAMPLE: <u>Dolphins</u> <u>leap</u>.

- Expand the meaning of a sentence by adding adjectives, adverbs, and prepositional phrases to the sentence base.

    EXAMPLE: **The sleek** dolphins **suddenly** leap **high into the air**.

A. Expand the meaning of each sentence base by adding adjectives, adverbs, and/or prepositional phrases. Write each expanded sentence.

1. (Dinner cooks.) _____

2. (Clown chuckled.) _____

3. (Car raced.) _____

4. (Dancer spun.) _____

5. (Panthers growled.) _____

6. (Leaves fall.) _____

7. (Bread baked.) _____

8. (Lake glistened.) _____

9. (Ship glides.) _____

B. Write five sentence bases. Then write an expanded sentence containing each sentence base.

1. _____

   _____

2. _____

   _____

3. _____

   _____

4. _____

   _____

5. _____

   _____

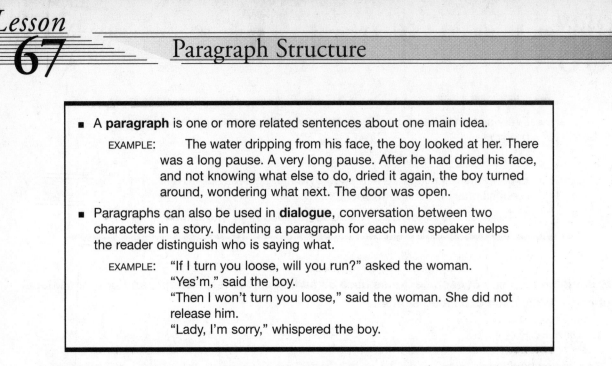

- A **paragraph** is one or more related sentences about one main idea.

    EXAMPLE: The water dripping from his face, the boy looked at her. There was a long pause. A very long pause. After he had dried his face, and not knowing what else to do, dried it again, the boy turned around, wondering what next. The door was open.

- Paragraphs can also be used in **dialogue**, conversation between two characters in a story. Indenting a paragraph for each new speaker helps the reader distinguish who is saying what.

    EXAMPLE: "If I turn you loose, will you run?" asked the woman.
    "Yes'm," said the boy.
    "Then I won't turn you loose," said the woman. She did not release him.
    "Lady, I'm sorry," whispered the boy.

In the following excerpt from the story "Save the Moon for Kerdy Dickus" by Tim Wynne-Jones, dialogue and narrative paragraphs have been joined together. Rewrite the passage with paragraphs so the transitions from narrative to dialogue are clear to the reader. Remember to indent where necessary.

He took a sip of the tea. His eyes cleared a bit. "Dad's in the truck," he said. "Oh, my!" said Barbara. "Where? We should get him." The Stranger nodded his big bear head in the direction that the truck was but, of course, you couldn't see it from the house. Ky looked down the driveway, but there is a bend in it so she couldn't see the road. Tan turned off the gas under the frying pan and was heading toward the closet for his coat. "I'll bring him back," he said. "No!" said the Stranger. His voice cracked a little. "He's okay. He's sleepin'. Truck's warm."

_____

_____

_____

_____

_____

_____

_____

_____

_____

_____

Lesson
68

> ■ A **topic sentence** is the sentence within a paragraph that states the main idea. It is often placed at the beginning of a paragraph.
>
> EXAMPLE:
>
> **The trip to the national park was a great success.** First, the visitors learned a lot from their guide about the park. They learned that the forest was created by people, not by nature. To their surprise, they found out that the park had more than five hundred species of plants. Then they went on a hike and even spotted a hawk flying overhead. Finally, the visitors had a wonderful picnic lunch and headed back home.

A. Write a topic sentence for each paragraph below.

1. Some jewellery is made out of feathers, leather, shells, or wood. Other jewellery is crafted from gold, silver, brass, copper, or other metals. Gems and unusual stones are added for their beauty and value.

Topic Sentence: _____

2. A pet goldfish needs clean water. A pump should be placed in the water to supply fresh air. The water temperature must be constant, and it must not go below 27°C. The goldfish should be fed flaked fish food or small insects.

Topic Sentence: _____

3. When Jana crawls over to a kitchen cabinet, she whips the door open to see what's behind it. With a little help from Jana, the pots and pans are on the floor in no time. If she sees a bag of groceries, Jana has to investigate the contents. After she is tucked in bed for the night, this toddler loves to climb out of her crib and explore.

Topic Sentence: _____

B. Write a topic sentence for each of the paragraph ideas below.

1. birthday parties _____

2. a great adventure _____

3. a great hockey player _____

4. a favourite holiday _____

5. homework _____

6. video games _____

7. vacations _____

8. the Olympics _____

> ■ The idea expressed in a topic sentence can be developed with sentences containing **supporting details**. Details can include facts, examples, and reasons.

A. Circle the topic sentence, and underline three supporting details in the paragraph below.

Many people in animal rights groups believe that animals should not be used for food, clothing, cosmetic testing, or medical experiments. Many activists believe that humans in most parts of the world no longer need to eat meat or wear animal skins to survive. They also argue that many species, such as whales, rhinos, and tigers, are on the way to extinction. If too many species disappear forever, animal rights activists and other environmental groups fear that the ecology of the planet will suffer extreme damage.

B. Answer the following questions about the supporting details you underlined.

   1. What is one supporting detail that is a fact?

   _____

   _____

   _____

   2. What is a supporting detail that is a reason?

   _____

   _____

   _____

C. Read each topic sentence below, and write three supporting details for each.

   1. Earth is a planet in trouble.

   _____

   _____

   _____

   2. People who care about environmental issues can do many things to help.

   _____

   _____

   _____

> - One way to organize information in a paragraph is to put it in **chronological order**—the time in which events occurred. Words such as <u>first</u>, <u>next</u>, <u>second</u>, <u>then</u>, <u>finally</u>, and <u>later</u> are used to indicate the order in which events happen.
>   EXAMPLE: **First**, the architect drew up plans. **Then** she presented the plans to council.
>
> - Another way to organize information is to use **spatial order**. Words such as <u>above</u>, <u>near</u>, <u>over</u>, <u>beside</u>, <u>right</u>, <u>left</u>, <u>closer</u>, <u>farther</u>, <u>up</u>, and <u>down</u> are used to express spatial relationships.
>   EXAMPLE: The **top** floor will include a skylight. **Below**, a greenhouse will allow more natural light.

A. Read each paragraph below and tell whether it is in chronological order or spatial order. For the paragraph in chronological order, underline the time order words. For the paragraph in spatial order, underline the words that indicate spatial order.

1. The developer must first propose the idea for a cinema complex to city council. Then the council must approve the developer's proposal, which includes the architect's design. Next, the developer will establish a final budget and schedule. Finally, construction can begin.

   Order: _____

2. The cinema complex includes six gigantic screening rooms, an entertainment arcade, and a food court. The food court will be located near the entrance beside the arcade. Escalators will lead to the screening rooms on the top floor.

   Order: _____

B. Number the details below in chronological order.

____ Next, in early January, the construction budget was finalized.

____ Then construction began at the beginning of April.

____ The complex finally opened to the public in late October.

____ In early November, council approved the developer's proposal.

C. Choose one of the scenes below. Write a paragraph of at least four sentences describing the scene. Use spatial order words to show location.

Scenes: your room, a hockey arena, a favourite store, a friend's house

_____

_____

_____

- **Transitions** are words or phrases that connect ideas. Transitions help the reader clearly understand relationships such as time, space, emphasis, example, contrast, comparison, effect, and addition. The words or phrases under the bold headings are examples of transition words that help ideas flow smoothly and coherently.

time	space	emphasis	example
before	here	in fact	for instance
contrast	**comparison**	**effect**	**addition**
however	likewise	consequently	furthermore

A. Indicate in the blank what type of relationship each transition word or phrase shows.

1. during _____

2. similarly _____

3. indeed _____

4. there _____

5. in fact _____

6. accordingly _____

7. moreover _____

8. nevertheless _____

9. for example _____

10. on the other hand _____

11. clearly _____

12. next _____

B. The following paragraph has no transition words or phrases. Rewrite it with transition words or phrases to improve its coherence.

No person can live in the world alone. Each person depends on hundreds of others to provide the basic needs of food and transportation. We depend on people for love and understanding. There are times when we need to be on our own with nature and our inner thoughts. We need to reach a balance between being alone and being with others. We will find happiness.

_____

_____

_____

_____

_____

_____

_____

Topic and Audience

> ■ The **topic** of a story or an article is the subject written about.
>
> ■ The **audience** is the group of readers.
>
>   EXAMPLES: students, family members, neighbours, readers of a newspaper

A. Choose the most likely audience for each topic listed below.

a. kindergarten students   **b.** federal politicians   **c.** Grade 9 students   **d.** parents

_____ **1.** Olympic Snowboarder Speaks at Kelowna High School

_____ **2.** Local Education Taxes on the Rise

_____ **3.** Franklin the Turtle at Library Story Hour

_____ **4.** Literacy Tests Required for Grade 10 Students

_____ **5.** Canada's Exports to United States Decline

_____ **6.** Fire Chief Visits Elementary Schools

_____ **7.** Dance Cancelled Due to Exam Schedule

_____ **8.** Budget Surplus Announced by Federal Government

_____ **9.** Tryouts for Basketball Team on Thursday

_____ **10.** Block Parents Discuss Strategies

B. Read the paragraph below. Then answer the questions that follow.

> On Wednesday evening, April 13 at 8:00, Martin Babula of the Silver Blades Hockey School will speak about the summer program offered at Teen Arena in Caledonia. His talk will include hockey camp details for July and August, successful graduates of the program, and enrolment costs. Mr. Babula's well-known program has been established since 1992, attracting NHL hopefuls throughout the province.

1. What is the topic of the paragraph?

_____

2. Name two possible audiences for the paragraph.

_____

3. Explain why each audience might be interested.

Audience 1:

_____

Audience 2:

_____

Clustering

■ A **clustering diagram** shows how ideas relate to a particular topic. The topic is written in the centre. Related ideas are written around the topic. Lines show the connections between the ideas.

safety — wilderness camping — equipment

enjoyment — costs — parks

Topic Sentence: Wilderness camping has become a popular pastime.

A. Read each paragraph below. Notice the underlined topic sentence as you read. Then fill in each cluster to show how the details relating to that topic sentence could have been chosen.

1.   Committee members worked hard to organize the concert. They hired musicians, printed tickets, booked a hall for the evening, and took out a large ad in a local newspaper. Then they made sure that the sound system was working.

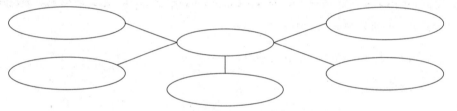

2.   Volunteers offered to restore the old railway station. Engineers made sure that the building was structurally sound, and electricians updated the wiring. Other workers came to paint the station exterior, varnish the woodwork, and give the place a thorough cleaning.

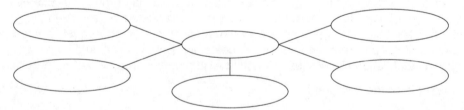

B. Write a topic in the centre of the cluster below. Then fill in the cluster with details that would support your main topic.

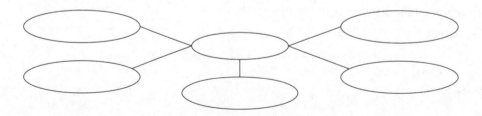

- Before you write, organize your thoughts by making an **outline**. An outline consists of the title of the topic, headings for the main ideas, and subheadings for the supporting details.

- Main headings are listed after Roman numerals. Subheadings are listed after capital letters. Details are listed after Arabic numerals.

EXAMPLE:

Topic	Should Everyone Have the Internet?
Main heading	I. Benefits to business
Subheadings	A. Huge customer base
	B. Money saved on expensive rents
Main heading	II. Benefits to public
Subheading	A. Lots of information available
Details	1. Researchers can find up-to-date data
	2. Students can access many topics
Subheading	B. People can communicate more easily

Choose a topic that interests you. Then write an outline for that topic, using the example outline as a guide.

_____

_____

_____

_____

_____

_____

_____

_____

_____

_____

_____

_____

_____

Persuasive Writing

> ■ The writer of a **persuasive composition** tries to convince others to accept a personal opinion.

A. Read the following persuasive composition.

More Affordable Housing Needed

Many people in Canada desperately need housing that they can afford. During the last decade a larger gap has opened between wealthy Canadians and poorer ones. Working people who were once able to afford decent shelter find that low wages do not stretch as far as they did. In many large cities, rent increases have out-paced wage increases. For example, a worker making $8 an hour may have trouble feeding a family and paying $600 a month for rent. In some cases, low-income housing has been torn down to make room for expensive high-rise condominiums. When poor families have no place to go, they may end up in shelters or on the streets.

The solution to the problem is not easy. Governments at various levels have to watch their spending. However, if the problem gets worse, rising health costs and crime rates may result. These problems also carry high price tags.

B. Answer the questions below.

1. List three facts the writer includes to persuade the reader.

_____

_____

_____

_____

_____

2. List two reasons the writer includes in the composition.

_____

_____

_____

3. List one example the writer uses to support the topic.

_____

_____

_____

C. **Choose one of the topic sentences below. Write a short paragraph in which you use facts to persuade your audience about the topic.**

    1. Canada is the best place in the world to live.

    2. Penalties for drinking and driving should be tougher.

_____

_____

_____

_____

_____

D. **Choose one of the topic sentences below. Write a short paragraph in which you use reasons to persuade your audience about the topic.**

    1. Having a good education is important.

    2. The most exciting sport is _____ .

_____

_____

_____

_____

_____

E. **Choose one of the topic sentences below. Write a short paragraph in which you use an example to persuade your audience about the topic.**

    1. I know someone who showed a lot of courage.

    2. Movies are great entertainment.

_____

_____

_____

_____

_____

_____

Revising and Proofreading

- **Revising** gives you a chance to rethink and review what you have written and to improve your writing. Revise by adding words and information, by taking out unneeded words and information, and by moving words, sentences, and paragraphs around.

- **Proofreading** has to do with checking spelling, punctuation, grammar, and capitalization. Use proofreader's marks to show changes needed in your writing.

Proofreader's Marks

≡	⊙	SP
Capitalize	Add a period	Correct spelling
/	∧	¶
Make a small letter	Add something	Indent for new paragraph
∧	ℓ	⟶
Add a comma	Take something out	Move something

A. Rewrite the paragraph below. Correct the errors by following the proofreader's marks.

¶ banff national park is the oldest park national in canada. it became a national park in 1885. It is located in the hart of the rocky mountains on the british columbia/alberta boarder. Trans-Canada Highway #1 runs thruogh the Park. banf national park is 6641 square km, and contains magestic mountain Peaks, hoodoos, hot springs, great valeys, dense forests, alpin meadows, glasial lakes, and spectecular rivers. the park park atracts over 4.5 visitors every year. people enjoy montaineering, skiing, cycling, hiking, fishing, canoing, kayaking, and Photograpy in the natural beautiful setting. Sum environmentalists beleive that the many visitors actualy threaten the the Ecology of the park.

_____

_____

_____

_____

_____

_____

B. Read the paragraphs below. Use proofreader's marks to revise and proofread the paragraphs. Then write your revised paragraphs below.

although banff national park may be the best-known National park in canada, 38 other national parks our also poplar with visitors national parks are found in evry part of the country from as far North as ellesmere Island to Point pelee in the most sothern part of canada the total area of the national system park is as large as as the canadian Grate Lakes, or three times big as the province of nova scotia

if you have a chance visit a national park in your regoin of canada you may live closest to Gros Morne national perk a UNESCO World Heritage Site amid Newfoundland and Labroador's wild natural beauty maybe your home is near Grasslands national park in Saskatcewan, where visitors can sea rare prarie grasses dinosaur fosils, and badlands. People who want to know more about canada's northern regions may go to Nahanni in the Northwest territries Vuntut in the Yukon, or or Sirmilik national Park on Baffin island. national parks are natonal treasures

_____

_____

_____

_____

_____

_____

_____

_____

_____

_____

_____

_____

A. Expand the sentence bases below by adding adjectives, adverbs, and prepositional phrases.

    1. (Crowd cheered.)

    _____

    2. (Eagles flew.)

    _____

    3. (Baby laughed.)

    _____

B. Read the paragraph below. Then circle the topic sentence, and underline only the supporting details.

        Some days of the week are snowier than others, depending on where you live. Toronto and Edmonton get the most snow on Thursdays. Halifax, Montréal, and Vancouver have the most snow on Saturdays. Wednesday is the warmest day worldwide. The snow pattern may be caused by workday air pollution, which produces more condensation—and more precipitation.

C. Complete the cluster for the topic given in the centre.

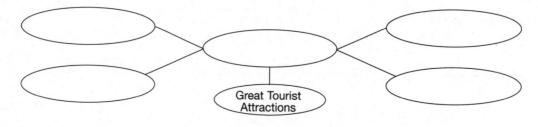

Great Tourist Attractions

D. Begin an outline based on that cluster.

Topic: Great Tourist Attractions

    I. _____

        A. _____

        B. _____

    II. _____

        A. _____

        B. _____

E. Organize the items in sequence and write in outline form.

Topic: How to create an ad

Use computer software to produce final copy

Decide on the message

Choose a product, idea, or service

Logical steps to follow

Target an audience

Design the ad

Combine message and design

_____

_____

_____

_____

_____

_____

_____

F. Read the persuasive paragraph. Then answer the questions below.

Eat Less Junk Food

    Chips, pop, and chocolate bars may be tasty snacks, but too much junk food is bad for your body. Eating junk food deprives the body of the protein, vitamins, and minerals it needs to perform well. The empty calories in junk food can also make you gain weight. A large high-calorie "snack" can take up as much as 50% of a person's daily calorie requirements!

1. What is one reason the writer gives for advising readers to avoid junk food?

_____

2. What example does the writer give to support the argument?

_____

G. Read the paragraph below. Use proofreader's marks to revise and proofread the paragraph. Then write your revised paragraph below.

Robots our no longer the creatoin of sceince fiction righters their are are hundreds of thousands of

robots in the world today some are little moor then medal arms others have sensors and camras

what do robots do they errands run in Hospitals and they patrol buildings night robots have bean

on the moon andd on mars to.

_____

_____

_____

_____

_____

A. Choose one of the topic sentences below. Write a short paragraph in which you use facts to persuade your audience about the topic.

   1. More people should use public transportation.

   2. Advertising is sometimes misleading.

   3. Getting in shape is worth the effort.

_____

_____

_____

_____

_____

B. Choose one of the topic sentences below. Write a short paragraph in which you use reasons to persuade your audience about the topic.

   1. All high-school students should take driver-education courses.

   2. Experience is often the best teacher.

   3. Electronic technology will not replace books.

_____

_____

_____

_____

_____

C. Choose one of the topic sentences below. Write a short paragraph in which you use an example to persuade your audience about the topic.

   1. Many species are disappearing from our planet.

   2. Special effects bring movies alive.

   3. Multiculturalism has worked well in Canada.

_____

_____

_____

_____

_____

D. Choose another topic from Exercises A, B, or C. Write a statement for a composition in which you wish to persuade your audience to consider your idea about the topic.

_____

_____

E. Write a short outline of your ideas. Include main headings, subheadings, and details.

_____

_____

_____

_____

_____

_____

_____

_____

_____

_____

F. Write the first and second paragraphs of a short composition that persuades people about your idea. Use the outline you wrote as a guide. Then revise your paragraphs, and proofread them.

_____

_____

_____

_____

_____

_____

_____

_____

_____

_____

_____

- A **dictionary** is a reference book that contains definitions of words and other information about their history and use.
- **Entries** in a dictionary are listed in **alphabetical order**.
- **Guide words** appear at the top of each dictionary page. Guide words show the first and last entry on the page.

    EXAMPLE: The word pine would appear on a dictionary page with the guide words pinball / pink. The word pipe would not.

A. **Put a check in front of each word that would be listed on the dictionary page with the given guide words.**

1. frozen / gather	2. money / muscle	3. perfect / pin
_____ fruit	_____ muddy	_____ perfume
_____ grain	_____ moss	_____ pit
_____ furnish	_____ motorcycle	_____ pick
_____ gate	_____ mustard	_____ photo
_____ gallop	_____ moisten	_____ pest
_____ former	_____ moose	_____ plastic
_____ forgive	_____ museum	_____ pillow
_____ fuzz	_____ morning	_____ pile
_____ galaxy	_____ mortal	_____ pipe
_____ future	_____ modest	_____ pizza

B. **Number the words in each column in the order in which they would appear in a dictionary. Then write the words that could be the guide words for each column.**

1. _____ / _____	2. _____ / _____	3. _____ / _____
_____ raccoon	_____ seize	_____ octopus
_____ radar	_____ shellfish	_____ olive
_____ rabbit	_____ shrink	_____ of
_____ raisin	_____ signal	_____ office
_____ react	_____ silent	_____ old
_____ reflect	_____ scent	_____ odour
_____ rebel	_____ shuffle	_____ once
_____ rainfall	_____ shaft	_____ oil
_____ relay	_____ serpent	_____ odd
_____ remind	_____ seldom	_____ onion
_____ refuse	_____ scope	_____ occasion
_____ ran	_____ selfish	_____ only

- A **syllable** is a part of a word that is pronounced at one time. Dictionary entry words are divided into syllables to show how they can be divided at the end of a writing line.

- A **hyphen** (-) is placed between syllables to separate them.
  EXAMPLE: el-e-gant

- If a word has a beginning or ending syllable of only one letter, do not divide it so that one letter stands alone.
  EXAMPLES: a-part; nos-y

A. Find each word in a dictionary. Then write each word with a hyphen between each syllable.

1. tomorrow _____
2. carriage _____
3. business _____
4. meddle _____
5. character _____
6. factory _____
7. pollution _____
8. variety _____
9. gallant _____
10. brother _____

11. preparation _____
12. enthusiasm _____
13. embarrassment _____
14. security _____
15. laboratory _____
16. machine _____
17. varnish _____
18. significant _____
19. fragrant _____
20. indemnity _____

B. Write two ways in which each word may be divided at the end of a writing line.

1. dramatic _____ _____
2. recognize _____ _____
3. permanent _____ _____
4. excellent _____ _____
5. employment _____ _____
6. potential _____ _____
7. barometer _____ _____
8. ferocious _____ _____

- Each dictionary entry word is followed by a spelling in parentheses that shows how the word is **pronounced**.
- **Accent marks** (´) show which syllable or syllables are said with extra stress.
- A **pronunciation** key (shown in box below) shows some of the other symbols used to explain pronunciations of words.

A. Use the pronunciation key to answer the questions.

1. Which word tells you how to pronounce the e in heel?

   _____

2. How many words are given for the symbol ə?

   _____

3. What letters are used for the sound of the u in use?

   _____

4. What symbol would be used for the sound of u in up?

   _____

5. What symbol would be used for the sound of ch in chin?

   _____

[mi] me; [pɪrs] pierce	[fɔrk] (fork)
[ɪt] it	[ɔɪl] (oil)
[eip] ape	[ould] (old)
[ɛnd] end	[pʊl] (pull)
[kɑrt] cart	[rul] (rule)
[ʌp] up	[θɪn] (thin)
[əis] ice; [wəit] (white)	[ðɪs] (this)
[ʌut] out	[tʃɪn] (chin)
[ə'bʌv] above	[ʃɒp] (shop)
[tɜrn] turn	['trɛʒər] (treasure)
[hɒt] hot; [sɒŋ] song	[juz] (use)

The symbol ə stands for the unstressed vowel sound in about, taken, pencil, lemon, and circus

B. Use the pronunciation key to help you choose the correct word for each spelling given in parentheses. Underline the correct word.

1. (boun)   bone   ban   bond
2. (mit)   met   meat   mate
3. (wɒd)   woad   wade   wad
4. (rid)   read   red   raid
5. ('watər)   waiter   whiter   water
6. (heit)   hat   height   hate
7. (nɛl)   nail   knell   kneel
8. (dʌm)   dim   dumb   doom
9. (fir)   fear   far   fir
10. (lard)   lured   lard   lord
11. (frəit)   freight   fruit   fright
12. (bun)   bun   boon   bound

© 2000 Gage Educational Publishing Company   Unit 6, Study Skills

- A dictionary lists the **definitions** of each entry word. Many words have more than one definition. In this case, the most commonly used definition is given first. Sometimes a definition is followed by a sentence showing a use of the entry word.

- A dictionary also tells the **part of speech** for each entry word. An abbreviation (shown in box below) stands for each part of speech. Some words may be used as more than one part of speech.

  EXAMPLE: **por-tion** ('pɔrʃən) *n.* **1.** A part or share: *We spent a portion of the day at the park. -v.* to divide into parts or shares.

Use the dictionary entries below to answer the questions.

frag-ment ('frægmənt) *n.* **1.** a broken piece. **2.** an incomplete or disconnected part: *We could hear only fragments of the conversation. –v.* to break or divide into fragments.

fra-grant ('freɪgrənt) *adj.* giving off a pleasing odour: *Roses in bloom are wonderfully fragrant.*

frail (freil) *adj.* **1.** not very strong: *He was in frail health.* **2.** easily broken, damaged, or destroyed.

3. liable to yield to temptation. *–n.* a basket made of rushes, used for gathering fruit etc.

frank (fræŋk) *adj.* **1.** free in expressing one's thoughts, opinions and feelings. **2.** undisguised, plain: *The crew carried out a frank mutiny. -v.* **1.** send (letters, packages) without charge. **2.** mark for free mailing: *Have the letters been franked? -n.* a mark to show that a letter or parcel is to be sent without charge.

1. Which words can be used as either a noun or a verb?

   _____

n.	noun
pron.	pronoun
v.	verb
adj.	adjective
adv.	adverb
prep.	preposition

2. Which entry word has the most example sentences?

   _____

3. What part of speech is <u>fragrant</u>? _____

4. How many definitions are given for the word <u>fragrant</u>?_____

   for <u>frail</u>? _____

   for <u>frank</u>? _____

5. Write the most commonly used definition of <u>frank</u>. _____

6. Use the second definition of <u>frail</u> in a sentence. _____

7. Write a sentence in which you use <u>fragment</u> as a verb. _____

8. Write a sentence in which you use <u>frank</u> as a noun. _____

> ■ An **etymology** is the origin and development of a word. Many dictionary entries include etymologies. The etymology is usually enclosed in brackets [ ].
>
> EXAMPLE: **knit** [ME *knitten* < OE *cnyttan*, to knot]. The word knit comes from the Middle English word <u>knitten</u>, which came from the Old English word <u>cnyttan</u>, meaning "to tie in a knot."

Use these dictionary entries to answer the questions.

cam-pus ('kæmpəs) *n.* the grounds and buildings of a school or university. [Latin *campus*, meaning field, perhaps because most colleges used to be in the country.]

chaise longue ('ʃeiz 'lɒŋ) *n.* a chair with a long seat which supports the sitter's outstretched legs. [French *chaise*, chair + *longue*, long.]

gar-de-nia (gɑr'dinjə) *n.* a fragrant yellow or white flower from an evergreen shrub or tree. [Modern Latin *Gardenia*, from Alexander *Garden*, 1730-1791. U.S. scientist who studied plants.]

pas-teur-ize ('pæstʃəraɪz) *v.* to heat food to a high temperature in order to destroy harmful bacteria. [From Louis *Pasteur*, inventor of the process.]

rent (rɛnt) *n.* a regular payment for the use of property. [Old French *rente*, meaning taxes.]

ut-ter ('ʌtər) *v.* to express; make known; put forth. [From Middle English or Dutch, *utteren*, literally, out.]

wap-i-ti ('wɒpɪti) *n.* the North American elk. [From the Algonquian name *wapitā*, meaning white, referring to the animal's white rump and tail.]

1. Which word comes from an Algonquian word?_____

2. What does the Algonquian word mean? _____

3. Which word was formed from the name of an inventor? _____

4. Which words come from French words? _____

5. What do the French words <u>chaise</u> and <u>longue</u> mean? _____

6. Which word was formed from the name of a scientist? _____

7. Which word comes from a colour? _____

8. Which words come from Latin words? _____

9. Which word comes from a Middle English word? _____

10. What does the French word <u>rente</u> mean? _____

11. Which word comes from two languages? _____

12. What does the word <u>utteren</u> mean? _____

13. What does the Latin word <u>campus</u> mean? _____

14. Which word is the name of a flower? _____

15. Which word names a piece of furniture? _____

Lesson 82 — Using Parts of a Book

- A **title page** lists the name of a book and its author.
- A **copyright page** tells who published the book, where it was published, and when it was published.
- A **table of contents** lists the chapter or unit titles and the page numbers on which they begin. It is at the front of a book.
- An **index** gives a detailed list of the topics in a book and the page numbers on which each topic is found. It is in the back of a book.

A. Answer the questions below.

1. Where should you look for the page number of a particular topic? _____

2. Where should you look to find out who wrote a book? _____

3. Where should you look to get a general idea of the contents of a book? _____

4. Where should you look to find out the year of publication? _____

5. Where should you look to find the name of the book? _____

6. Where should you look to find out who published a book? _____

B. Use your *Language Power* book to answer the questions.

1. What company published this book? _____

2. How many units are in this book? _____

3. On what page does Unit 4 start? _____

4. How many pages are in Unit 1? _____

5. What is the copyright date? _____

6. What pages contain lessons on prepositions? _____

7. On what page does Unit 6 start? _____

8. On what pages are the lessons on nouns found? _____

9. What lesson is on page 34? _____

10. List the pages that teach pronouns. _____

11. On what page is the lesson on word origins found? _____

12. On what page is the lesson on conjunctions found? _____

13. On what pages is the lesson on proofreading? _____

- A **chart** lists information in columns, which you read down, and in rows, which you read across. The information can be either words or numbers.

- A **graph** shows how quantities change over time. It often shows how two or more things change in relation to one another. The information can be shown through the use of lines, dots, bars, pictures, or in a circle.

A. Use the chart and the graph to answer the following questions.

Maximum Daily Temperature Chart
in Degrees Celsius

Month of the Year	Athens, Greece	Sydney, Australia
January	13	26
March	16	25
May	25	19
July	33	16
September	19	20
November	11	24

1. Which month is the hottest in Athens? _____ in Sydney? _____

2. Which month is the coolest in Athens? _____ in Sydney? _____

3. Which months have the same temperature in Athens and in Sydney?

_____

4. Which city has the more extreme temperature range? How do you know?

_____

_____

5. Do you find the graph or the chart easier to read?

Why? _____

_____

6. Does the graph or the chart represent change over time more accurately?

_____

- A **road map** is another valuable type of visual aid. Maps like the one shown below are helpful when you are unfamiliar with a certain area. To use any map, you should refer to its **legend**, **compass rose**, and **scale**.

- The legend tells what each symbol represents.

- The compass rose is made up of arrows that point north, south, east, and west.

- The scale allows you to determine how far it is from one location to another. To use the scale, mark the distance between any two locations along the edge of a sheet of paper. Then place the sheet of paper alongside the scale of distance, lining up one of the marks with zero. This will allow you to read the distance between the two locations.

B. Use the map to answer the questions below.

Maple Falls

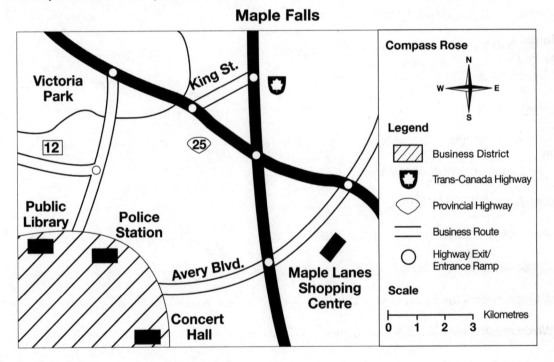

1. Which direction from the business district is Victoria Park? _____

2. On what road is the shopping centre? _____

3. How many kilometres is it from the Police Station to the Concert Hall? _____

4. What kind of highway is 25? _____

5. Does Business Route 12 run north/south or east/west? _____

6. Is the Public Library within the business district? _____

7. How many exit ramps are there on Highway 25 from Avery Blvd. to Victoria Park? _____

8. How many kilometres is it from Victoria Park to the Maple Lanes Shopping Centre? _____

■ Books are arranged on library shelves according to **call numbers**. Each book is assigned a number from 000 to 999, according to its subject matter. The following are the main subject groups for call numbers:

000-099 Reference	500-599 Science and Mathematics
100-199 Philosophy	600-699 Technology
200-299 Religion	700-799 The Arts
300-399 Social Sciences	800-899 Literature
400-499 Languages	900-999 History and Geography

A. Write the call number group in which you would find each book.

1. *India: The Land and Culture* _____

2. *Today's Technology* _____

3. *French Made Easy* _____

4. *Math Puzzles* _____

5. *Medieval Thought* _____

6. *The Canadian Global Almanac* _____

7. *Canadian Artists of the 1960s* _____

8. *Poems to Persuade* _____

9. *Chemistry Experiments* _____

10. *Women in Society* _____

11. *Chinese Folk Tales* _____

12. *A Study of Buddhism* _____

13. *The War of 1812* _____

14. *The Canadian Encyclopedia* _____

15. *Observing Primates in the Wild* _____

B. Write the titles of three of your favourite non-fiction books. Write the call number range beside each title.

1. _____

2. _____

3. _____

- An **encyclopedia** is a reference book that contains articles on many different topics. The articles are arranged alphabetically. Each volume is marked to show which articles are inside.
- Guide words are used to show the first topic on each page in a print resource. Electronic resources use a key word search.
- At the end of most articles there is a listing of **cross-references** to related topics for the reader to investigate.

A. Find the entry for Terry Fox in an encyclopedia. Then answer the following questions.

1. What encyclopedia did you use? _____

2. When did Terry Fox live? _____

3. Where was he born? _____

4. Where did he begin his famous journey? _____

5. For what is he best remembered? _____

B. Find the entry for Larch in an encyclopedia. Then answer the following questions.

1. What encyclopedia did you use? _____

2. Where does the eastern larch tree grow? _____

3. By what other name is it sometimes known? _____

4. What is special about this tree? _____

5. How tall do most larches grow? _____

C. Find the entry in an encyclopedia for a famous person who interests you. Then answer the following questions.

1. Who is your subject? _____

2. When did the person live? _____

3. Where did the person live? _____

4. Why is the person famous? _____

5. What else would you like to know about this person? _____

_____

6. What cross-references are listed? _____

> - A **thesaurus** is a reference book that writers use to find more precise or alternate words. A thesaurus lists words in alphabetical order. Each entry has a list of **synonyms**. Many thesauri (the plural of *thesaurus*) provide synonyms for using a word as a noun, verb, adjective, or adverb. Some thesauri provide **antonyms** or words that have opposite meanings. Many word processing programs contain a thesaurus option.
> - You can use a thesaurus to improve the quality of your sentences, making them more descriptive.
>   EXAMPLE: **Original:** Trevor walked slowly across the room and said that he was angry.
>   **Improved sentence:** Trevor sauntered across the room and bellowed his anger.

A. Use a thesaurus to find two synonyms for each of the following words.

cage _____ _____   displeasure _____ _____

observe _____ _____   beloved _____ _____

difficult _____ _____   move _____ _____

serious _____ _____   poor _____ _____

angry _____ _____   promise _____ _____

B. Use a thesaurus to find synonyms for the underlined words. If you can't find a word, check for its root, or common synonyms that you know. Rewrite the sentences using the most appropriate synonyms.

1. The Singhs were very happy after winning their big lottery prize.

_____

_____

2. The centre fielder ran toward the fence, jumped for the ball, and caught it to save the game.

_____

3. He could never get a word in because his uncle talked constantly.

_____

4. The children laughed as the tiny puppy licked their faces.

_____

5. I was so hungry that I ate my lunch quickly.

_____

- An **atlas** is a reference book that uses maps to organize pertinent facts about provinces, countries, continents, and bodies of water. Additional maps show information on topography; resources, industry, and agriculture; vegetation; population; climate; and history.

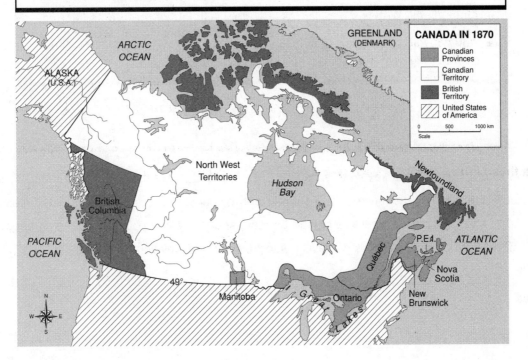

Use the sample atlas entry to answer the questions below.

1. What part of the world is shown on this map?

   _____

2. This is a historical map. What time in history does it depict?

   _____

3. Name the three oceans shown on this map.

   _____

4. To which country did British Columbia belong in 1870?

   _____

5. Name two areas that were Canadian provinces in 1870.

   _____

6. Is Nova Scotia to the east or west of Ontario?

> - The **World Wide Web** is an international computer network that contains an overwhelming amount of data.
> - **Search engines** such as Yahoo and Lycos organize information and allow users to move from site to site using a system of **hypertext links**.
> - Although the **Web** is a popular research tool with lots of up-to-date information, using it can be frustrating if the search is not specific and focussed. EXAMPLE: Entering the key words <u>sports cars</u> may yield thousands of "hits." Entering the key word <u>Porsche</u> narrows the search.

1. Choose a topic approved by your teacher. What search engine did you access? _____

   What key word(s) did you use? _____

2. How many sites did your key word(s) find? _____ Narrow the search if the list is too long.

3. Choose the Web site that seems the most relevant to your topic. If the site does not contain what you need to know, go back in your search and be more specific. When you have found an appropriate Web site, write three sentences containing information that is relevant to your topic.

   _____

   _____

   _____

   _____

4. How is the information relevant to your topic?

   _____

5. Who is the author of the Web site?

   _____

6. What is the address of the Web site?

   _____

7. When was the site last updated?

   _____

8. Does the site provide links to other useful information?

   _____

9. If there are graphics, do they load quickly? _____ Do they enhance the text?

   _____

10. Would you recommend this site to other students interested in this topic? Why or why not?

    _____

- Use a **dictionary** to find the definitions of words and pronunciations of words, suggestions for word usage, and etymologies or word histories.
- Use an **encyclopedia** to find articles about many different people, places, and other subjects. Use an encyclopedia to find references to related subjects.
- Use a **thesaurus** to find synonyms and antonyms.
- Use an **atlas** to find maps and other information about geographical locations.
- Use the **World Wide Web** to find very current information that may not be available from other sources.

A. Write dictionary, encyclopedia, thesaurus, atlas, or World Wide Web to show where you would find the following information.

_____ **1.** the life of Louis Riel

_____ **2.** the latest information on genetically modified food

_____ **3.** the provinces through which the Saskatchewan River runs

_____ **4.** the origin of the word moccasin

_____ **5.** today's weather forecast for Rome, Italy

_____ **6.** the most direct route from Rimouski to Fredericton

_____ **7.** a synonym for the word sleepy

_____ **8.** the meaning of the word lapidary

_____ **9.** recent information on the subject of air pollution

_____ **10.** the pronunciation of the word khaki

_____ **11.** the life of Carl Jung

_____ **12.** an antonym for the word delicious

_____ **13.** the Battle of Britain in World War II

_____ **14.** an article on gold mining

_____ **15.** the current National Hockey League standings

_____ **16.** the meaning of the word reprisal

_____ **17.** the biography of James Naismith

_____ **18.** the location of the Canadian Shield

B. Follow the directions, and answer the questions.

1. Choose a city you would like to know more about.

   Name of city: _____

2. List three reference sources that you can use to find information about this city.

   a. _____

   b. _____

   c. _____

3. Find information about the city in one of the reference sources you listed.

   Write the exact title of the reference source.

   _____

4. Write a short summary of the information you found.

   _____

   _____

   _____

   _____

   _____

5. Find information about the city in one other reference source.

   Write the exact title of the reference source.

   _____

6. What new information did you find about the city?

   _____

   _____

   _____

C. Follow the directions, and answer the questions below.

1. In what province or territory do you live? _____

2. Find information about your province or territory in one of the reference sources. Write the exact title of the reference source. _____

3. Write a short summary of the information you found.

   _____

   _____

   _____

   _____

 Unit 6, Study Skills

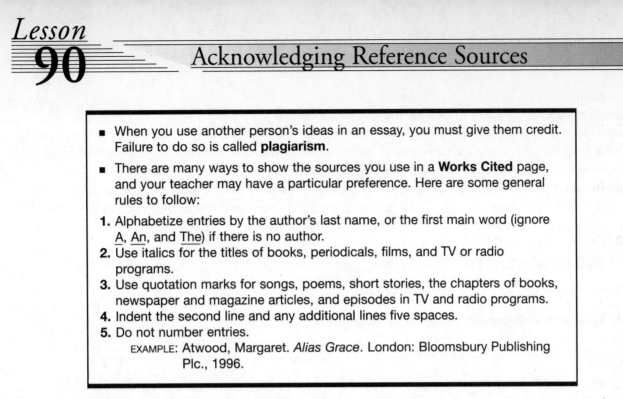

- When you use another person's ideas in an essay, you must give them credit. Failure to do so is called **plagiarism**.
- There are many ways to show the sources you use in a **Works Cited** page, and your teacher may have a particular preference. Here are some general rules to follow:

1. Alphabetize entries by the author's last name, or the first main word (ignore A, An, and The) if there is no author.
2. Use italics for the titles of books, periodicals, films, and TV or radio programs.
3. Use quotation marks for songs, poems, short stories, the chapters of books, newspaper and magazine articles, and episodes in TV and radio programs.
4. Indent the second line and any additional lines five spaces.
5. Do not number entries.
   EXAMPLE: Atwood, Margaret. *Alias Grace*. London: Bloomsbury Publishing Plc., 1996.

Place the following entries in correct order for a Works Cited page. Be sure to organize each entry according to the format shown in the example. Use underlining to show italics.

The Outsiders by S. E. Hinton. New York: Viking, 1967.

"Montreal Canadians" by James Marsh. *The Canadian Encyclopedia*. 1988 edition.

"The Future of Ecotourism." World Wide Web. 28 June 1998.

Gage Canadian Student Writer's Guide by Chelsea Donaldson. Toronto: Gage Educational Publishing Company, 2000.

"The Visitor" by Dylan Thomas. *The Collected Stories*. New York: New Directions Publishing Inc., 1984.

Smart Cooking by Anne Lindsay. Toronto: Macmillan Canada, 1986.

_____

_____

_____

_____

_____

_____

_____

_____

_____

A. Use the dictionary entries to answer the questions below.

tux-e-do (tʌkˈ sidou) *n.* a man's formal suit, usually black, having a jacket with satin lapels and trousers with a stripe of satin along the outer side of each leg. [From *Tuxedo* Park, New York, an exclusive community where this suit was popular during the nineteenth century.]

twin (twɪn) *n.* **1.** one of two offspring born at the same birth. **2.** either of two people, animals, or things that are very much or exactly alike. *–adj.* **1.** being one of two born as twins. **2.** being one of two things that are very much or exactly alike: *The fort had twin towers. –v.* to give birth to twins.

1. What part of speech is tuxedo? _____

2. How many definitions are given for tuxedo? _____

3. How many definitions are given for the noun twin? _____

4. Which word can be used as an adjective? _____

5. Which word comes from the name of a place? _____

6. How many syllables are there in tuxedo? _____

   In twin?) _____

7. What parts of speech is twin? _____

8. Underline the pair of words that could be guide words for the dictionary entries above.

   a. turtle / twill

   b. twang / twist

   c. tusk / twirl

   d. Tuscan / twig

n.	noun
pron.	pronoun
v.	verb
adj.	adjective
adv.	adverb
prep.	preposition

B. Write the part of the book you would use to answer the following questions.

1. What is the name of Chapter 2? _____

2. Who wrote the book? _____

3. When was the book published? _____

4. Does the book have information on Mahatma Gandhi? _____

C. Use the sample thesaurus entry below to answer the questions.

kindly *adj.* **syn.** agreeable, benevolent, gentle
ant. cruelly, ungraciously, unkindly

1. What is the entry word? _____

2. What are its antonyms? _____

3. Write one of its synonyms in a sentence. _____

D. Use the map to answer the questions.

Compass Rose

Legend

═══ Business Route

○ Highway Exit/ Entrance Ramp

⬭ Provincial Highway

Scale

0 1 2 3 Kilometres

Jade River

Riverside Road

Fairgrounds

46

Zoo

To City

Franklin Point

1. Which direction is the zoo from the fairgrounds? _____

2. What kind of highway is 46? _____

3. How far is it from the exit on Riverside Drive to the fairgrounds? _____

4. How wide is the Jade River? _____

E. Write dictionary, encyclopedia, thesaurus, atlas, or World Wide Web to show where you would find the following information.

1. the most direct route from Collingwood, Ontario to Boston, Massachusetts _____

2. the pronunciation of the word poignant _____

3. an antonym for the word perilous _____

4. the life of Pierre Elliott Trudeau _____

5. information on tours to Alaska _____

6. the vegetation of Australia _____

F. Organize the following entries in correct format for a Works Cited page. Use underlining to show italics.

A Good House by Bonnie Burnard. Toronto: HarperCollins, 1999.

"Canada's Literary Legacy" by Gordon Pitts. *Globe and Mail.* 14 Feb. 2000.

"The Outlaw" by Sinclair Ross. *The Lamp at Noon and Other Stories.* Toronto: McClelland & Stewart, 1996.

"The Table" by Rosemary Sullivan. *Blue Panic.* Windsor: Black Moss, 1991.

_____

_____

_____

_____

A. Find the word <u>advance</u> in your dictionary. Then follow the directions and answer the questions.

1. Write the guide words from the page on which you found the entry for <u>advance</u>. _____

2. Write <u>advance</u> in syllables. _____

3. As what parts of speech can <u>advance</u> be used? _____

4. Write the history of the word. _____

_____

B. Write the call number group in which you would find each book. You may wish to review the call number classification system on page 116.

_____ 1. *The Production of Steel*

_____ 2. *Battles of the Ancient World*

_____ 3. *German for Beginners*

_____ 4. *Social Trends in Canada*

_____ 5. *Jewish Theology*

_____ 6. *Colombo's Canadian Quotations*

_____ 7. *The Characteristics of Sea Mammals*

_____ 8. *Eastern Philosophy*

_____ 9. *Photography as Art Form*

C. Use a thesaurus to find a synonym for each underlined word.

_____ _____ 1. The man was so <u>angry</u> he <u>shook</u>.

_____ _____ 2. We <u>saw</u> a <u>lovely</u> sunset from the bridge.

D. Use the encyclopedia sample to answer the questions.

KIM CAMPBELL was Canada's first female Prime Minister. She was born in Port Alberni, British Columbia in 1947. Campbell received a degree in political science, later studying law. After being elected in the federal riding of Vancouver Centre in 1988, she joined Brian Mulroney's cabinet. She served as Attorney General and Minister of Defence before being elected leader of the Conservative Party in 1993. On June 25, 1993, she was sworn in as Canada's nineteenth Prime Minister. *See also* PRIME MINISTERS OF CANADA.

1. What is this article about?

_____

2. What did Campbell study at university?

_____

3. What part of Canada did she represent in federal politics?

_____

4. How many years was she in federal politics before becoming Prime Minister?

_____

5. Under what subject heading can you find related information?

_____

E. Use the information in the chart to complete the graph. Then answer the questions.

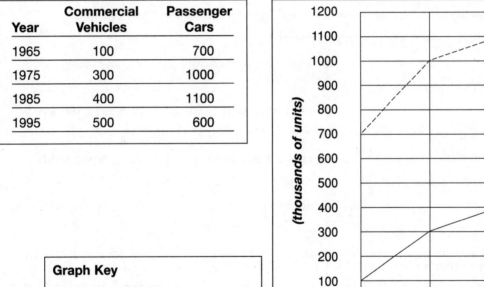

New Vehicle Sales
(thousands of units)

Year	Commercial Vehicles	Passenger Cars
1965	100	700
1975	300	1000
1985	400	1100
1995	500	600

New Vehicle Sales
(thousands of units)

Graph Key

Commercial Vehicles ——————

Passenger Cars – – – – – – –

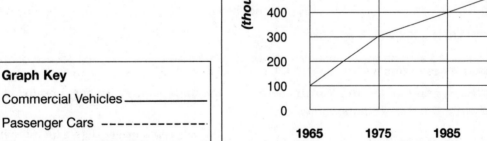

1. How many passenger cars were sold in 1985? _____

2. What was the total number of vehicle sales in 1965? _____

3. What year had the highest number of commercial vehicles sold? _____

4. What year had the lowest number of passenger vehicles sold? _____

5. What trends in vehicle sales can be learned from this data? _____

_____

Synonyms ■ On the line before each pair of words, write <u>S</u> if they are synonyms.

_____ 1. arrogant, conceited

_____ 2. initiate, commence

_____ 3. joyous, dismal

_____ 4. fashionable, dowdy

_____ 5. mourn, lament

_____ 6. stress, anxiety

_____ 7. humid, muggy

_____ 8. mediate, intervene

_____ 9. elaborate, simple

Homophones ■ Underline the correct homophones in each sentence below.

1. We always (by, buy) (plain, plane) food when our (ant, aunt) visits.

2. While in Washington, he managed to (meat, meet) a friend in the (capital, capitol) building.

3. The rabbit had black (hair, hare), small (pause, paws), and a fluffy (tail, tale).

Homographs ■ Circle the letter for the best definition for each underlined homograph.

1. The holiday gave Antonia a <u>rest</u> from studying chemistry.

   a. part left over   **b.** freedom from activity   **c.** not moving

2. The privilege is not of our <u>desert</u>.

   a. to abandon   **b.** dry, barren land   **c.** what is deserved

3. The golf <u>club</u> had a benefit dance to raise money.

   a. a heavy wooden stick   **b.** an organization of people   **c.** a playing card

4. The solarium is <u>light</u> because it has many windows.

   a. bright   **b.** not heavy   **c.** come down to the ground

5. Climbing stairs is a <u>tax</u> on a weak heart.

   a. money paid to support government   **b.** burden or strain   **c.** accuse or charge

Prefixes, Suffixes, and Compound Words ■ Write <u>P</u> if the underlined word has a prefix, write <u>S</u> if it has a suffix, and write <u>C</u> if it is a compound word.

_____ _____ 1. Padma was <u>careless</u> riding her bike <u>downhill</u>.

_____ _____ 2. The <u>softball</u> player is <u>hopeful</u> about winning the championship.

_____ _____ 3. <u>Rethink</u> your plan. It seems incredibly <u>selfish</u>.

_____ _____ 4. When the goalie sprained his ankle, his <u>teammates</u> were <u>helpless</u>.

_____ _____ 5. They were <u>unhappy</u> with the <u>hazardous</u> driving conditions.

_____ _____ 6. Because of the <u>downpour</u>, we were <u>unable</u> to eat in the park.

_____ _____ 7. The club decided to <u>reschedule</u> the tennis match for the next Saturday <u>afternoon</u>.

Contractions ■ **Write the contraction for each pair of words.**

1. will not _____

2. she is _____

3. they have _____

4. I am _____

5. I will _____

6. you are _____

7. do not _____

8. you had _____

9. you will _____

10. there is _____

11. have not _____

12. is not _____

Connotation and Denotation ■ **For each underlined word, write (-) for a negative connotation, (+) for a positive connotation, or (N) for a neutral connotation.**

_____ **1.** Tara scribbled a reply.

_____ **2.** What story did Lise tell?

_____ **3.** She brags about her family's wealth.

_____ **4.** The joke Abida told was hilarious.

_____ **5.** The professor's lecture was tedious.

_____ **6.** The teacher smiled primly at the class.

_____ **7.** We left the waiter a puny tip.

_____ **8.** Cam fought his illness courageously.

_____ **9.** I expect to receive a large raise.

_____ **10.** The boss hollered at the worker's mistake.

_____ **11.** Rusalka is an accomplished musician.

_____ **12.** The painting was very famous.

_____ **13.** We plodded home after the game.

_____ **14.** The restaurant serves scrumptious salads.

_____ **15.** She arrived early.

Idioms ■ **Underline the idiom in each sentence. Then write the meaning of the idiom on the line.**

1. The lost CD turned up in my room yesterday. _____

2. I was in the doghouse for a month after the incident. _____

3. My father's business is on the skids. _____

4. If we put our heads together, we can solve the problem. _____

5. Binh let the cat out of the bag when he mentioned the surprise party. _____

6. She was in hot water after she failed two exams. _____

7. The good news from her coach put her on cloud nine. _____

8. Julia was in a bind when she accepted two invitations for one evening. _____

Types of Sentences ■ Before each sentence, write D for declarative, IN for interrogative, IM for Imperative, and E for exclamatory. Punctuate each sentence correctly.

_____ 1. This pasta is delicious _____

_____ 2. Please pass the butter_____

_____ 3. Who is the new chef _____

_____ 4. I'm ravenous _____

_____ 5. What's on the menu _____

_____ 6. Does anyone want bread_____

_____ 7. Ouch, I bit my lip _____

_____ 8. I'd like more salad _____

_____ 9. Chew more carefully _____

_____ 10. Who wants to do the dishes _____

Parts of a Sentence ■ Underline the word or words in each sentence that are identified in parentheses.

1. (compound predicate) Jean Paul typed and proofread his essay.

2. (indirect object) Ann, lend me your blue sweater.

3. (subject complement) The weather was excellent.

4. (direct object) The teacher gave the report an "A."

5. (subordinate clause) The first movie that Jeremy saw was a comedy.

6. (complete predicate) She read that book four times.

7. (complete subject) Everyone in the group spoke on a different topic.

8. (simple predicate) All the renovations were completed in two weeks.

9. (independent clause) We had to be on time, or we would lose our reservation.

10. (adverb clause) I showered before breakfast.

Parts of a Sentence ■ Underline each subordinate clause. Then write adjective or adverb on the line.

_____ 1. The doctor who performed the surgery was known for her skill.

_____ 2. The strike was over before the employees lost wages.

_____ 3. It was the first time that Gudrun had been to Vancouver Island.

_____ 4. Although it was still early, everyone left the party.

_____ 5. Alberta is a beautiful province that tourists like to photograph.

_____ 6. When Evan heard the news, he became very excited.

_____ 7. The fox bolted because it had never seen people before.

_____ 8. Security has become tighter since the airport discovered the bombs.

_____ 9. The boy whose ticket was drawn won a new car.

_____ 10. After the way they treated me, I don't want to work for them again.

Complex Sentences ■ **To each group of words below, add a subordinate clause or an independent clause to create a complex sentence.**

1. Our family rented a cottage _____

2. After it was morning _____

3. The situation was serious _____

4. When we took a trip to the Yukon _____

5. Before crossing the river _____

6. While stopping for ice cream _____

7. When he asked for help _____

8. No one had heard of the band _____

9. Six weeks later _____

10. Before the final concert _____

Compound Sentences ■ **Create compound sentences by adding an independent clause to each group of words.**

1. Clara bought a new snowmobile _____

2. She called to complain _____

3. It was too late for my mother_____

4. We chose to stay in the country_____

5. Representatives from several provinces came _____

6. You can find help there _____

7. It's possible that we are lost _____

8. The alarm sounded _____

Run-On Sentences ■ **Correct each run-on sentence by writing it as two sentences or as a compound sentence.**

1. It was a beautiful day, the sun was shining we woke up early.

_____

2. We are here for one reason, we need to discuss the company's future.

_____

Expanding Sentences ■ **Expand the sentence by adding details to answer the questions <u>What kind?</u> and <u>How many?</u> Write the expanded sentence on the line.**

The wind blew.

Parts of Speech ■ **Write the part of speech above each underlined word. Use the abbreviations given in the box.**

n.	noun
pron.	pronoun
v.	verb
adj.	adjective
adv.	adverb
prep.	preposition
conj.	conjunction

1. They ate baked salmon, steamed rice, and fresh asparagus for lunch.

2. The frightened children quickly gathered up their toys and headed home.

3. The Celtic band performed old traditional ballads and poems expressively.

4. Rayanne tried very hard to complete the history report, but she fell asleep.

5. The country's citizens silently watched social decline until the leader resigned.

Verbs ■ **Underline the correct verb in each sentence.**

1. Stamp collecting (is, are) Nick and Brett's favourite hobby.

2. The champion (received, will receive) her gold medal in an hour.

3. We (driven, drove) to town for groceries.

4. The council (has tried, have tried) to improve school facilities.

5. Mu Tan (chose, chosen) to take part in the run for cancer research.

6. The criminal (broken, broke) into the house to steal camera equipment.

7. The leader of the rebels (was, were) captured.

8. The fresh flowers (smells, smell) wonderful.

Pronouns ■ **Underline the pronoun in parentheses that agrees with the antecedent in each sentence. Circle each antecedent.**

1. Marco's parents gave him (their, his) advice.

2. The girls bought the pizza and shared (them, it).

3. The athlete was interviewed by journalists after (her, their) victory.

4. The children brought (their, they) pets to the contest.

5. Take the bird and release (it, him) into the wilderness.

Adjectives and Adverbs ■ **Complete each sentence with the proper form of the adjective or adverb in parentheses.**

1. (late) We arrived at school _____ than the other students.

2. (good) The hamburgers at the barbecue were _____ than the ones at the restaurant.

3. (fast) Is Charmaine the _____ member of the track team?

4. (bad) This is the _____ excuse for failure I've ever heard.

5. (fresh) Use this bread for the sandwiches because it is _____ than mine.

      Unit 3, Grammar and Usage

Grammar and Usage ■ **Fill in the blanks by supplying the word or words specified in parentheses.**

Whooping cranes _____ birds whose population is endangered. Also
(linking verb)

known as whoopers, these large birds are the _____ of all birds in
(superlative adjective)

North America. An adult male stands up to 1.5 m tall _____ can weigh up to
(conjunction)

7.5 kg. Despite their size, cranes _____ slow. They average 45 km per hour.
(contraction of are not)

In late April, cranes arrive at Wood Buffalo National Park, _____
(relative pronoun)

extends into northern Alberta from the Northwest Territories. By the end of September,

_____ leave for a _____ long 4000 km flight to the Aransas National
(pronoun)   (adverb)

Wildlife Range in Texas. By _____ on wind currents, they can stay in the air for 10 hours.
(present participle of glide)

Whooping cranes stay with the same mate for _____ . Wildlife
(noun)

biologists _____ the crane's elaborate courting rituals. _____
(present perfect of observe)   (limiting adjective)

female lays two eggs, and both adults incubate _____ . The chicks hatch at
(pronoun)

different times. The chicks _____ within 80-90 days.
(future tense of fly)

The _____ danger to cranes is collision _____ power
(superlative adjective)   (preposition)

lines during migration. Other factors include human development. The _____
(proper noun)

in Texas _____ , as is the whoopers' last breeding area in Wood Buffalo.
(protect in passive voice)

_____ , there are only 320 whooping cranes left in the _____ world.
(conjunction)   (adjective)

Wildlife biologists want to establish populations in new areas to ensure that the cranes

_____ any threat to their habitat.
(future tense of survive)

Capitalization and End Punctuation ■ Circle each letter that should be capitalized. Write the capital letter above it. Add the correct end punctuation to each sentence.

1. our neighbourhood holds a canada day celebration every july _____

2. will the speakers be dr. bain and ms. vishnu _____

3. That café, marcel's express, serves french pastry and ethiopian coffee _____

4. muriel street will be closed off on saturday and sunday for the lion's club parade _____

5. mr. herlihy of the store electronics galore is donating a prize to the draw _____

6. will the Italian restaurant on college street provide sandwiches _____

7. My best friend, Errol Kanhai, always says, "be the best you can be_____ "

8. will dancers and singers from the national culture centre perform scenes from william

   shakespeare's *twelfth night* _____

9. the bike race begins at the corner of church and main streets at 8:00 A.M. on saturday_____

10. the candidates represented women from nova scotia, québec, and newfoundland and labrador _____

Using Other Punctuation ■ Add commas, quotation marks, and apostrophes where needed in the sentences below.

1. Why are you telling me your troubles asked Kamal.

2. We used books encyclopedias atlases and the World Wide Web when doing research.

3. Ive spent three hours exercising puffed Geoffrey.

4. Ms. Denys said Youll find the next quiz much easier.

5. Sam Tai and Barbara are all going to Florida for March Break.

6. Wont you please spare some change pleaded the man at the bus station.

7. Shes the one said Veronika who organized the conference in Banff.

8. Subarus Hondas and Toyotas sell well in this city.

9. My Greek salad recipe he said calls for tomatoes onions cucumbers and feta cheese.

10. Jamal mowed the lawn weeded the garden and watered the flowers.

11. Saras car was in the shop for two weeks remarked her father.

12. Moira Rosa and Shanti went to Dianes birthday party.

Insert apostrophes, dashes, hyphens, semicolons, colons, parentheses, and ellipsis points where they are needed in the sentences below.

1. I cant find the sign up sheet listen Daphne did someone take it?

2. The well known restaurant is open between 11 00 and 2 00, serving the following lunch specialties spring rolls, hot sour soup, shrimp dumplings, and noodles.

3. JAN facing the audience Ive always stood up for my beliefs.

4. The car wouldnt start we walked home from the arena.

5. My mother in law helped us move into our fourth storey apartment.

6. They printed the following excerpts from the concert review His voice seemed strained, weak and thin the audience lost interest before intermission.

7. My great grandmother doesnt believe in slowing down she plays bridge three times a week even though shes eighty six years old.

8. Please dont forget the following school supplies pens, papers, erasers, and paper clips.

9. It's an emergency I can tell by his voice so get help quickly.

10. At 10 00 in the evening, the search party still hadnt found the missing child.

Circle each letter that should be capitalized. Add punctuation where needed.

r. r. 1,
orangeville, ON
l9w 2y8
February 15, 2000

dear mr. kappas

on saturday, may 6, the mono township conservation group will be holding its annual tree planting event _____ residents of the township will have the chance to pick up trees at the mono forest facility on county road 15 from 8 00 to 2 00 on that day _____ dozens of people maybe even hundreds will come by to pick up pine spruce and maple trees _____

is there a possibility you could donate some time to this event _____ i know that youre extremely busy but your help during last years event proved to be invaluable _____ if you do agree to help out your task could be one of the following take charge of the cash keep track of the number of trees sold or help people load their vehicles with trees _____ let me know if youd be willing to help out _____ you can reach me at 943 6666 after 6 00

Sincerely,

agnes sankar

Topic Sentences ■ **Write a topic sentence for the paragraphs below. Name a possible audience for each paragraph.**

1. All children and adults should learn basic first aid. Courses are offered through schools and community groups. You never know when you'll need to clean a wound or use a more difficult technique during an emergency. By knowing first aid, you'll always be prepared.

   Topic Sentence: _____

   Audience: _____

2. Butterflies and moths fly from flower to flower, looking for pollen. When they land on a flower, some of the sticky pollen rubs off on their legs. When they fly to another flower, it rubs off onto the new flower.

   Topic Sentence: _____

   Audience: _____

3. Many people walk or run to stay healthy. Others swim or play sports for exercise. Some people prefer indoor exercises, such as using exercise videos or machines.

   Topic Sentence: _____

   Audience: _____

Support Details ■ **Underline the two sentences that contain details that support the topic sentence.**

1. **Topic Sentence:** A meteor looks like a bright streak of light in the sky.

   a. A meteor leaves a trail of hot gas.

   b. A meteor blazes across the sky as it travels through space.

   c. I saw a meteor fall from the sky.

2. **Topic Sentence:** Ants are called social insects.

   a. Ants live together in colonies and help each other.

   b. Ants are pests, and they can ruin a picnic.

   c. Ants share their food and their work.

3. **Topic Sentence:** Alligators and crocodiles are alike in many ways.

   a. Alligators have wider heads and shorter jaws than crocodiles.

   b. They are both reptiles and have rough skin.

   c. Alligators and crocodiles live in and near water.

Revising and Proofreading • Rewrite the paragraphs below. Correct the errors by following the proofreader's marks.

Proofreader's Marks

≡ Capitalize	⊙ Add a period	(SP) Correct spelling
/ Make a small letter	∧ Add something	¶ Indent for new paragraph
∧ Add a comma	ℓ Take something out	⟶ Move something

¶ did you know that roughly three-quarters of the earth's fresh water is held not in rivers and lakes? the water is

held in glaciers; lage sheets of ice that form in high altitudes and polar regions, such as antarctica and

Greenland there are between 70,000 and 200,000 glaicers in the world.

¶ as temperatures warm glaciers melt a little and move at a wrate that can't bee seen as they move they

sometimes freize and add to their mass before moving on they actually reshape The land they pass ovver the

most famus glaciers are in europe the best-known ones are in the french and swiss alps Glacier National Park

in the Selkirk mountains of Southeastern British Columbia has more four hundred glaciers.

_____

_____

_____

_____

_____

_____

_____

_____

_____

_____

_____

_____

_____

Using the Dictionary ■ **Use the dictionary entries to answer the questions.**

con-stant (ˈkɒnstənt) *adj.* **1.** always the same, not changing: *If you walk due north, your direction is constant.* **2.** never stopping. **3.** faithful, loyal. [Middle English from Old French from Latin *constare* to stand firm]

con-straint (kənˈstreint) *n.* **1.** confinement **2.** a holding back of natural feelings: *She kept her anger under constraint.* **3.** force, compulsion. [Middle English from Old French *constreinte*]

1. Circle the letter of the guide words for the above entry.

     a. conserve/consign   **b.** constable/construct   **c.** construe/consume

2. How many definitions are listed for constant? _____ constraint? _____

3. Write one sentence using the third definition of constant.

_____

4. Write one sentence using the first definition of constraint.

_____

5. What part of speech is constant? _____ constraint? _____

6. How many syllables does constant have? _____ constraint? _____

7. Which syllable is stressed in constant? _____ in constraint? _____

8. Which word traces its origins to Latin? _____

9. Write the spelling of how constraint is pronounced. _____

Parts of a Book ■ **Write <u>title page</u>, <u>table of contents</u>, or <u>index</u> to tell where you would find this information.**

_____ **1.** The page on which specific topics can be found.

_____ **2.** The book's name

_____ **3.** The page on which a chapter begins

Reference Sources ■ **Write <u>D</u> for dictionary, <u>E</u> for encyclopedia, <u>TH</u> for thesaurus, <u>AT</u> for atlas, or <u>WW</u> for World Wide Web to tell where you would find this information.**

_____ **1.** the current standing of the Toronto Raptors

_____ **2.** the etymology of the word lacrosse

_____ **3.** the history of the United Nations

_____ **4.** the distance between Edmonton and Calgary

_____ **5.** a synonym for the word sweet

Using Visual Aids ▪ Use the map to answer the questions.

Curzon Centre

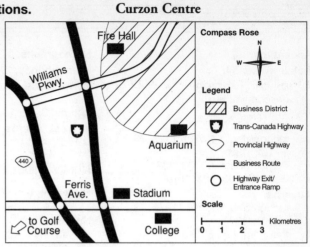

1. What direction is the college from the fire hall?

   _____

2. How far is it from the aquarium to the stadium?

   _____

3. Does Ferris Ave. run north/south or east/west?

   _____

Using an Encyclopedia ▪ Use the encyclopedia sample to answer the questions.

The GREAT DEPRESSION of the 1930s was worldwide, but its effects were felt especially in Canada. It began in October 1929 when wheat prices began to fall. In the same month the stock market collapsed, ruining thousands of shareholders. By 1930, the number of unemployed people had doubled. By 1933, one in five Canadians was unemployed.

Western Canada was hardest hit because of its reliance on wheat. The prairies also suffered from a drought that led to crop failure. In Saskatchewan, two-thirds of the province's population had to go on welfare or "relief." A group of unemployed workers, angry about Canada's economic plight, took the railway east to Ottawa to protest against the government.

In 1935 Mackenzie King defeated Prime Minister R. B. Bennett. Although economic conditions began to improve slowly, the effects of the Depression only faded with the outbreak of World War II in 1939. *See also* CANADA, HISTORY.

1. What is this article about?_____

2. When did the Great Depression take place? _____

3. What two events ushered in the Great Depression?_____

   _____

4. Which part of the country was most affected by the Depression?_____

   Why?_____

5. Which Prime Ministers were in office during the Great Depression?_____

6. What brought about the end of the Depression? _____

Using a Thesaurus ▪ Use the sample thesaurus entry in the box to answer the questions.

1. What is the entry word? _____

2. What part of speech is <u>refuse</u>? _____

3. What are its synonyms?_____

> *refuse v. **syn.*** decline, deny, reject, spurn
> ***ant.*** accept, allow

Index

Accent marks, 110
Active voice, 54, 71
Adjectives
    descriptive, 59
    limiting, 59, 133
    proper, 59, 74
    recognizing, 59, 70, 71, 72, 73,
      132, 133
    that compare, 60, 73, 133
    using, 63, 66, 104, 130
Adverbs
    recognizing, 61, 70, 71, 72, 73,
      132, 133
    that compare, 62, 73
    using, 63, 66, 69, 91, 104, 130
Antecedents, 55-57, 71, 73, 132
Antonyms, 118
Apostrophes, 6, 43, 80, 88, 89, 134,
135
Atlas, using, 119, 121, 125, 138

Book, parts of, 113, 124, 138

Capitalization, 74-75, 87, 88, 89, 90,
134, 135
Clauses
    adjective, 27, 36, 131
    adverb, 27, 36, 130
    independent, 25-27, 29, 33, 36,
      38, 77, 83, 84, 130, 131
    subordinate, 25-26, 27, 29, 33,
      36, 38, 57, 77, 130, 131
Clustering, 98, 104, 137
Colons, 84, 88, 89, 135
Commas
    in comma splice errors, 34, 36,
      38
    in compound sentences, 77
    in quotations, 79
    in series, 77, 83
    using, 77, 87, 89, 134
Compound words, 7, 12, 128
Conjunctions, 27, 68, 70, 71, 72, 77,
83, 132, 133
Connotation/Denotation, 8, 12, 14,
129
Contractions, 12, 129, 133

Dashes, 81, 85, 89, 135
Dictionary, using, 108-112, 117, 121,
124, 125, 126, 128, 138
Direct objects, 22, 23, 35, 37, 38
Double negatives, 69, 73

Ellipsis points, 86, 89, 135
Encyclopedia, using, 117, 121, 126,
138, 139
Exclamation marks, 76, 79

Homographs, 3, 11, 13, 128
Homophones, 2, 11, 13, 128
Hyphens, 82, 88, 89, 109, 135

Idioms, 9, 12, 14, 129
Indirect objects, 23, 24, 35, 37, 38,
130

Library, using, 116, 126

Modifiers, 67

Nouns
    abstract, 40, 73
    collective, 40, 52
    common, 39
    concrete, 40, 73
    plural, 41, 42, 70, 72, 73, 80
    possessive, 43, 70, 80, 85
    proper, 39, 73, 74, 133
    recognizing, 10, 39, 70, 132, 133
    singular, 41, 42, 80
    using effectively, 10, 14

Outlining, 99, 104, 105, 107

Paragraphs
    audience of, 97, 101, 106-107,
      136
    in dialogue, 92
    narrative, 92
    ordering information within, 95
    persuasive writing in, 100, 101,
      105, 106, 107
    supporting details in, 94, 99, 100,
      104, 136
    topic of, 97, 98, 99, 104, 107
    topic sentences in, 94, 98, 101,
      104, 106, 136
    transition words in, 96
Parentheses, 85, 89, 135
Participial phrases, 67, 73
Passive voice, 54, 72, 133
Periods, 76
Predicates
    complete, 18, 19, 20, 21, 35, 130
    compound, 21, 35, 37, 130
    simple, 19, 21, 35, 37, 91, 130
Prefixes, 4, 128
Prepositional phrases, 65, 66, 71,
72, 73, 91, 104
Prepositions, 64, 65, 70, 71, 132, 133
Pronouns
    antecedents for, 55, 56, 57, 71,
      72, 73, 132
    indefinite, 80
    recognizing, 70, 132, 133
    relative, 27, 57, 72, 133
Pronunciation key, 109
Punctuation, 33, 76, 77, 79, 88, 89-
90, 134

Question marks, 76, 79
Quotation marks, 78, 79, 86, 87, 89,
134

Reference sources
    acknowledging, 123, 125, 138
    using, 121, 122, 125, 138
Revising/Proofreading, 102-103,
105, 107, 137

Semicolons, 83, 89, 135

Sentences
    base, 91, 104
    combining, 30, 34, 35
    complete, 32, 35, 37
    complex, 29, 30, 35, 36
    compound, 28-30, 34, 35, 36, 38,
      131
    declarative, 16, 35, 37, 130
    exclamatory, 16, 35, 37, 130
    expanding, 31, 38, 91, 104, 131
    imperative, 16, 35, 37, 130
    interrogative, 16, 35, 37, 130
    inverted, 17, 37
    natural order, 17, 35, 37
    run-on, 33, 36, 38, 131
    simple, 15, 28, 30, 35, 37
    types of, 16, 130
    writing, 91
Sentence fragments, 32, 36, 38
Subjects
    complete, 18-19, 20, 21, 130
    compound, 20, 35, 37, 130
    simple, 19, 20, 91
Subject complement, 24, 35, 37, 38,
130
Subject-verb agreement, 52
Suffixes, 5, 11, 13, 128
Synonyms, 1, 118, 128

Thesaurus, using, 118, 121, 124,
125, 126, 138, 139

Usage, 50-51, 53, 58

Verbs
    action, 44
    linking, 44, 133
    perfect tenses, 46
    recognizing, 10, 70, 132
    tenses, 44-45, 47-49, 133
    using effectively, 10, 14
Visual aids, using, 114, 115, 124,
127, 139

World Wide Web, using, 120, 121,
125, 138
Writing process. *See* Paragraphs.